PRIMARY MATHEMATICS

Challenging
Word Problems

 **Marshall Cavendish** Education

 SingaporeMath.com Inc®

Published by Marshall Cavendish Education

An imprint of Marshall Cavendish International (Singapore) Private Limited

Times Centre, 1 New Industrial Road, Singapore 536196

Customer Service Hotline: (65) 6411 0820

E-mail: tmesales@sg.marshallcavendish.com

Website: www.marshallcavendish.com/education

First published 2010

Reprinted 2012 (twice), 2013

ISBN 978-981-285-531-2

Printed in Singapore

Distributed in the U.S.A. by SingaporeMath.com Inc

SingaporeMath.com Inc®

The Publisher would like to recognize the contribution of Jennifer Hoerst (Curriculum Advisor, SingaporeMath.com Inc)
to Primary Mathematics Challenging Word Problems.

Preface

PRIMARY MATHEMATICS Challenging Word Problems provides graded exercises for students of mixed abilities and challenging questions for better math students. This series is written to supplement Singapore's **Primary Mathematics** textbooks, both U.S. and Standards editions, distributed by SingaporeMath.com, Inc. for use in the U.S.A.

Adopting a topical approach in which mathematical concepts and skills are taught and reinforced, the **Challenging Word Problems** series serves to improve students' problem-solving skills and enhance their mathematical reasoning.

Each book in the series features the following:

- **Worked Examples** for each topic show common methods of solution used in the Primary Mathematics textbooks;

- **Practice Questions** allow students to apply and practice questions similar to the ones discussed in the Worked Examples and in the Primary Mathematics textbooks;

- **Challenging Problems** provide opportunities for more capable students to solve higher-order word problems and further develop their problem-solving skills;

- **Mixed Problems** allow students to test their understanding of the concepts discussed in earlier topics and in the Primary Mathematics textbooks;

- **Answers** allow teachers or students to check their answers to all practice exercises and challenging problems;

- **Worked solutions** provide commonly used methods of solving non-routine questions, while encouraging creative or intuitive ones as well.

A student's guide to using the **Challenging Word Problems** series effectively.

1. Read each question given in the Worked Example. Try to solve it before reading the solution.

2. If your solution is similar to the one given in the Worked Example, well done. If you have used a different method, yet have arrived at the same answer, great – you now have at least two methods of solving this question.

3. If your answer is different, look at your work again and figure out where you may have gone wrong.

4. If you have understood all the worked examples, proceed to the Practice Questions; then check your answers with the ones at the back of the book. Should you get stuck at any question, don't panic; go through it again. If you still find difficulty in solving the question, seek help from your friend or teacher.

5. If you have understood and solved all the Practice Questions, you are now ready to try the Challenging Problems. Do them on your own first. Seek help only if you need some hints or clarification.

6. Try to come up with similar questions and challenge your friends to solve them. For a given question, discuss some possible solutions that you may have used in arriving at the answer.

Contents

1 Addition and Subtraction

Worked Example 1

Arthur scored 258 points at a carnival game. Joel scored 84 more points than Arthur and 68 more points than Ruth. How many points did the three children score in total?

258

Arthur

84

Joel

?

68

Ruth

$258 + 84 = 342$

Joel scored 342 points.

$342 - 68 = 274$

Ruth scored 274 points.

$258 + 342 + 274 = 874$

The three children scored **874** points in total.

Worked Example 2

Ivan has 400 more stickers than Tom at first. He gives 300 stickers to Tom. Who has more stickers now? How many more?

Before

| | 400 |
| Ivan | |

Tom

After

| 100 |
| Ivan |

| 100 | ? |
| Tom |

300

$400 - 300 = 100$

$300 - 100 = 200$

Tom has **200** more stickers than Ivan now.

A common mistake is to take $400 - 300 = 100$, and say that Ivan has 100 more stickers than Tom.

Worked Example 3

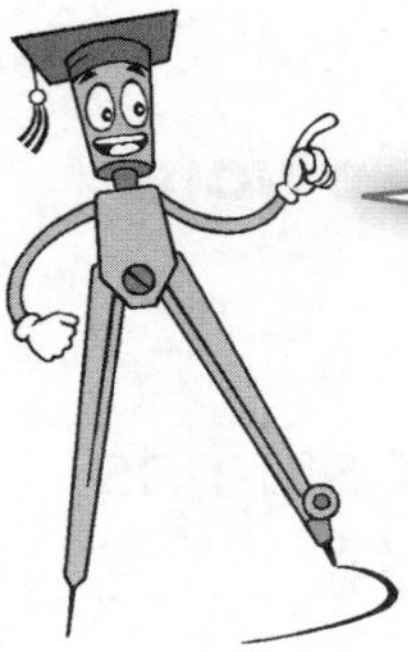

Sally had 57 more pencils than pens. After she gave away 47 pencils, she had twice as many pencils as pens. How many pens and pencils did she have left altogether?

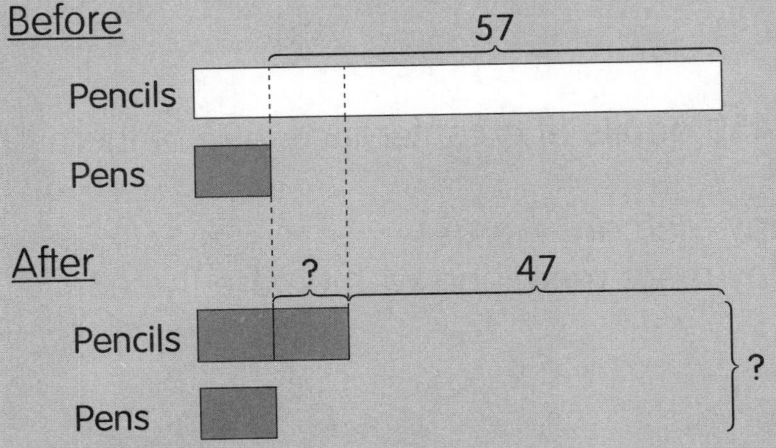

1 ■ ⟶ 57 – 47 = 10

3 ■ ⟶ 3 × 10 = 30

Sally had **30** pens and pencils left altogether.

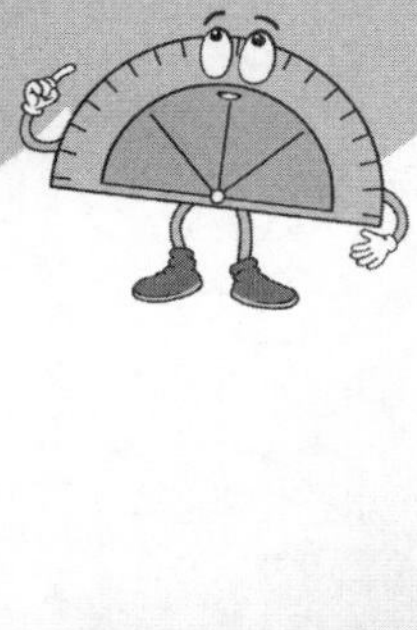

Practice Questions

Answer all questions. Show your work and write your statements clearly.

1. Joel collected 4352 stamps. He had 469 fewer stamps than Mark. How many stamps did Mark collect?

2. There are 2450 adults at a conference. 896 of them are women.
   (a) How many men are there?
   (b) How many more men than women are there?

3. Mr. Albert had $997. He planned to buy a plasma TV but was short of $498. How much did the plasma TV cost?

4. Arthur decided to read a 400-page novel. On the first day, he read 84 pages. On the second day, he read 107 pages and on the following day, he read 188 pages. How many pages were not read?

5. Fiona had 1638 stickers. Her cousin gave her 795 more stickers, she now has 208 fewer stickers than Dave.
   (a) How many stickers does Fiona have now?
   (b) How many stickers does Dave have?

6. Jill had 750 Singapore and Malaysia stamps altogether. She had 250 Singapore stamps. She gave away 165 Malaysia stamps. How many more Malaysia stamps than Singapore stamps did she have in the end?

7. A supermarket had 1260 apples, 960 oranges and 85 pears. If 978 apples, 875 oranges and 62 pears were sold, how many fruits were left?

8. How many times does the digit '0' appear in numbers from 1 to 100?

9. A movie theater has 1210 seats. During the first showing of a movie, 947 seats were taken. During the second showing, there were 139 empty seats. How many people watched the two showings altogether?

10. Steve has 500 more marbles than Richard at first. He gives 300 marbles to Richard. Who has more marbles now, and by how many?

Challenging Problems

Worked Example 1

I am thinking of a four-digit number. When I add all the digits, the sum is 17. What is the smallest possible number? (Do not begin the number with the digit '0'.)

Step 1:

Let the thousands digit be 1 and the hundreds digit be 0.

thousands	hundreds	tens	ones
1	0		

Step 2:

$$\underbrace{1 + 0}_{1} + \underbrace{\text{tens digit} + \text{ones digit}}_{16} = 17$$

$16 = 7 + 9$
$16 = 8 + 8$
$16 = 9 + 7$

Step 3:

$1 + 0 + 7 + 9 = 17$

Note that for the smallest possible number, the tens digit must be 7 and not 9.

The smallest possible number is **1079**.

Worked Example 2

Dennis wrote all the numbers from 300 to 400 on a notebook. How many times did he write the digit '3'?

Number	Number of '3's
300, 301, ...,399	100 (in the hundreds place)
330, 331, ...,339	10 (in the tens place)
303, 313, ...,393	10 (in the ones place)

$100 + 10 + 10 = 120$

He wrote the digit '3' **120** times.

Note that
$99 - 0 + 1 = 100$
$9 - 0 + 1 = 10$

Answer all questions. Show your work and write your statements clearly.

1. The sum of P and Q is 1023 greater than Q. The sum of P and Q is 549 greater than P.
   (a) What is the value of P?
   (b) What is the value of Q?
   (c) What is the sum of P and Q?

2. Laval is 18 years older than Chris. How old will Chris be when Laval is three times as old as Chris?

3. Jerry and Rick collect toy cars. Rick has 12 more toy cars than Jerry. They have 32 toy cars altogether. How many toy cars does Jerry have in his collection?

4. How many times does the digit '9' appear in the numbers from 1 to 100?

5. In the addition below, the letters P, Q, R and S stand for a one-digit number each.

$$\begin{array}{r} P\ Q \\ +\ R\ S \\ \hline 1\ 5\ 9 \end{array}$$

What is the value of P + Q + R + S?

6. Alberta saw 15 wild cats and flamingoes at the zoo. He counted their legs and found that there were 44 legs altogether. How many wild cats did he see at the zoo?

7. Abel saved 43 more nickels than dimes. After he spent 17 dimes, he had twice as many nickels than dimes. How many coins does he have left?

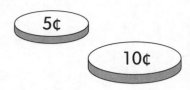

8. A baker sold a total of 1320 loaves of bread in June and July. He sold 678 loaves in June and 901 loaves in August. How many more loaves did he sell in August than in July?

9. How many whole numbers between 1 and 100 contain the digit '6'?

10. You have a sheet of postage stamps. The stamps are connected in five rows with five stamps in each row. What is the least number of times you can tear to get all the stamps apart?
(Hint: The stamps can be torn apart at the perforations between them. Several layers of stamps can be torn apart at one time if the perforations are lined up.)

2 Multiplication and Division

Worked Example 1

Each boy has 7 stickers and each girl has 6 stickers. How many stickers do 9 boys and 8 girls have in total?

Boys

$9 \times 7 = 63$

9 boys have 63 stickers.

Girls

$8 \times 6 = 48$

8 girls have 48 stickers.

$63 + 48 = 111$

9 boys and 8 girls have **111** stickers in total.

Worked Example 2

A total of 348 pears are put equally into 6 boxes. If 19 pears are then removed from one box, how many pears are left in that box?

$348 \div 6 = 58$

There are 58 pears in each box.

$58 - 19 = 39$

39 pears are left in that box.

Worked Example 3

Mrs. Azikou has 9 albums of 108 stamps each. She rearranges all the stamps equally into 6 larger albums. How many stamps will there be in each of the larger albums?

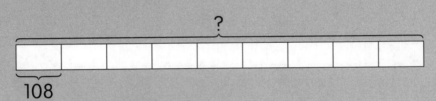

$108 \times 9 = 972$

There are 972 stamps altogether.

$972 \div 6 = 162$

There will be **162** stamps in each of the larger albums.

Practice Questions

Answer all questions. Show your work and write your statements clearly.

1. Each student receives 6 coins and each teacher receives 7 coins. How many coins do 8 students and 5 teachers receive altogether?

2. Mrs. Mendez and Miss Holders were distributing 120 pens equally among 8 children. How many pens did each child receive?

3. Mr. Golbout arranged 544 apples equally into 8 boxes. If he took out 29 apples from one box, how many apples would be left in that box?

4. Mr. Levoko has 7 bags of 126 coins each. He transfers all the coins into 3 bigger bags. How many coins will each bigger bag contain?

5. Bobby has 345 postcards. He gives 36 postcards to each of his 4 cousins. How many postcards does he have left?

6. Steve has 32 stickers. Joe has three times as many stickers as Steve but half as many stickers as Arlette. How many stickers does Arlette have?

7. Each album has 120 stamps. In each album, there are 42 Canada stamps, 50 U.S. stamps and the rest are Mexico stamps. How many Mexico stamps do 6 such albums have in total?

8. For every paper crane Ann makes, Sally can make 2 paper cranes. If they make 141 paper cranes altogether, how many paper cranes are made by Sally?

9. There are some tricycles and 12 bicycles in a repair shop. If there are 63 wheels altogether, how many tricycles are there in the shop?

10. Teddy and Sally each spend $800 of their salaries every month and save the rest. Teddy saves $250 each month and after two months, he has saved $80 more than Sally.
(a) How much does Sally save each month?
(b) What are Teddy's and Sally's salaries each month?

11. A bag of candies can be divided equally among 3, 4 or 5 children with no remainder. What is the least possible number of candies in the bag?

12. A watch costs $35 more than three identical clocks. Each clock costs $42. How much will 6 such watches cost?

Challenging Problems

Worked Example 1

Elsa and Mary collected a total of 20 empty bottles.
For every 2 empty bottles Elsa collected, Mary collected 3.
How many empty bottles did each girl collect?

Method 1

Elsa	Mary	Total
2	3	5
4	6	10
6	9	15
8	12	20

From the table, Elsa collected **8** empty bottles and
Mary collected **12** empty bottles.

Method 2

$2 + 3 = 5 \longrightarrow$ 1 group of 5 bottles
$20 \div 5 = 4$

There are 4 groups of 5 bottles.
$4 \times 2 = 8$ and $4 \times 3 = 12$

Elsa collected **8** empty bottles and Mary collected
12 empty bottles.

Worked Example 2

Gregory has 480 stamps. Steven has 260 stamps. How many stamps must Gregory give to Steven so that they have the same number of stamps? How many stamps will each of them have after sharing?

Method 1

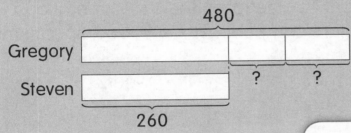

480 − 260 = 220
220 ÷ 2 = 110
Gregory must give Steven **110** stamps.
480 − 110 = 370 and 260 + 110 = 370
Each of them will have **370** stamps after sharing.

> There is a difference of 220 stamps.

Method 2

Total number of stamps = 480 + 260
                       = 740

740 ÷ 2 = 370
Each of them will have **370** stamps after sharing.
480 − 370 = 110
Gregory must give Steven **110** stamps.

Worked Example 3

Dr. Sumo and his two colleagues each can perform three operations every day. How many operations can they perform in a week?

Dr. Sumo and his two colleagues make up 3 doctors.

In 1 day, 3 doctors can perform $3 \times 3 = 9$ operations.
In 7 days, 3 doctors can perform $7 \times 9 = 63$ operations.

They can perform **63** operations in a week.

Answer all questions. Show your work and write your statements clearly.

1. Mrs. Smith goes into a store and orders a total of 85 blue and green balloons for her daughter's birthday. However, she wants 25 more green than blue balloons. How many balloons of each color will she take home?

2. Adam had 568 postcards and his sister, Sue, had 384 postcards. Adam gave his sister some postcards so they now have the same number. How many postcards do each of them now have?

3. A train that serves two remote villages is 142 meters long. It has 8 cars, each 16 meters long. What is the distance between two neighboring cars, if the distance between the cars is the same?

4. A bus can carry 48 passengers. How many buses will be needed to carry 120 passengers? How many seats will be unoccupied?

5. Mrs. Jiminez gave some students 4 candies each. She was then left with 8 candies. How many students received candies from Mrs. Jiminez if she had 84 candies at first?

6. After giving 16 coins to Melissa, Juan had twice as many coins as Melissa. If they had 144 coins altogether, how many coins did Juan have at first?

7. Rita had 24 more barrettes than Zoe. After she gave 5 barrettes to Zoe, Rita had twice as many barrettes as Zoe. How many barettes did Rita have left?

8. Jason and Louis picked up a total of 25 cans. For every 2 cans that Jason picked up, Louis picked up 3 cans. How many cans did each boy pick up?

9. There are some red envelopes containing 6 stamps each. There are also some blue envelopes containing 5 stickers each. What is the least possible number of red envelopes and blue envelopes that have as many stamps as stickers?

10. In order to make a rock bear, 1 large rock is used for the body and 5 small rocks are used for the head and legs. Jack has 9 large rocks and 20 small rocks. How many rock bears can he make?

3 Mental Calculation

Worked Example 1

Do the following additions mentally.
(a) 28 + 9
(b) 157 + 99

(a) $28 + 9 = 28 + 10 - 1$
$= 38 - 1$
$= \mathbf{37}$

(b) $157 + 99 = 157 + 100 - 1$
$= 257 - 1$
$= \mathbf{256}$

Look for friendly numbers like 10 and 100.
$9 = 10 - 1$
$99 = 100 - 1$

Worked Example 2

Calculate the following subtractions mentally.
(a) 187 − 98
(b) 705 − 399

(a) Method 1

$$187 - 98 = 187 - 100 + 2$$
$$= 87 + 2$$
$$= \mathbf{89}$$

Method 2

$$187 - 98 = 189 - 100$$
$$= \mathbf{89}$$

Increase both numbers by 2.

(b) Method 1

$$705 - 399 = 706 - 400$$
$$= \mathbf{306}$$

Method 2

$$705 - 399 = 706 - 1 - 399$$
$$= 706 - 400$$
$$= \mathbf{306}$$

Method 3

$$705 - 399 = 705 - 300 - 99$$
$$= 405 - 99$$
$$= 405 - 100 + 1$$
$$= 305 + 1$$
$$= \mathbf{306}$$

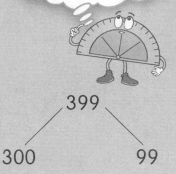

Increase both numbers by 1.

399
300   99

Can you think of other methods to subtract mentally?

Worked Example 3

Perform the following multiplications mentally.
(a) 45×6 (b) 607×8
(c) 25×9

(a) **Method 1**

$$45 \times 6 = 40 \times 6 + 5 \times 6$$
$$= 240 + 30$$
$$= \mathbf{270}$$

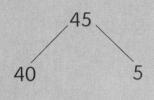

(b) **Method 2**

$$607 \times 8 = 600 \times 8 + 7 \times 8$$
$$= 4800 + 56$$
$$= \mathbf{4856}$$

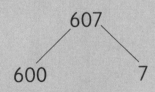

(c) **Method 1**

$25 \times 9 = 25 \times 10 - 25 \times 1$
$ = 250 - 25$
$ = \mathbf{225}$

Look for friendly numbers like 10 and 100.
$9 = 10 - 1$

Method 2

$25 \times 9 = 25 \times 4 + 25 \times 4 + 25 \times 1$
$ = 100 + 100 + 25$
$ = \mathbf{225}$

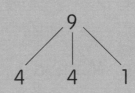

Method 3

$25 \times 9 = 20 \times 9 + 5 \times 9$
$ = 180 + 45$
$ = \mathbf{225}$

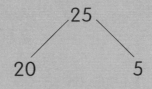

Practice Questions

Answer all questions.

Do the following mentally.

1. 56 + 9

2. 728 + 98

3. 145 − 99

4. 706 − 198

5. 25 × 6

6. 35 × 8

7. 198 + 243

8. 752 − 303

9. 505 × 9

10. 82 × 6

11. 57 × 3

12. 209 × 7

13. 49 × 5

14. 809 × 3

Challenging Problems

Worked Example 1

Do the following additions mentally.

(a) 137 + 48 + 63
(b) 56 + 36 + 68
(c) 488 + 356
(d) 998 + 703

(a) 137 + 48 + 63
= 137 + 63 + 48
= 200 + 48
= **248**

Add friendly numbers first.

(b) 56 + 36 + 68
= 56 + 30 + 4 + 2 + 68
= 56 + 4 + 30 + 2 + 68
= 60 + 30 + 70
= **160**

Look for an easier addition.

(c) 488 + 356
= 488 + 12 + 344
= 500 + 344
= **844**

356
12   344

(d) 998 + 703
= 998 + 2 + 701
= 1000 + 701
= **1701**

703
2   701

Worked Example 2

Do the following subtractions mentally.

(a) 6000 − 348   (b) 142 − 80   (c) 142 − 85

(a) 6000 − 348 = 5999 − 348 + 1
$\qquad\qquad$ = 5651 + 1
$\qquad\qquad$ = **5652**

6000 = 5999 + 1

(b) 142 − 80 = 42 + 100 − 80
$\qquad\qquad$ = 42 + 20
$\qquad\qquad$ = **62**

100 − 80 = 20

(c) 142 − 85 = 42 + 100 − 85
$\qquad\qquad$ = 42 + 15
$\qquad\qquad$ = **57**

100 − 85 = 15

Worked Example 3

Do the following multiplications and divisions mentally.

(a) 46 × 5   (b) 165 × 5
(c) 38 ÷ 2   (d) 190 ÷ 5

(a) 46 × 5 = 46 × 10 ÷ 2
$\qquad\quad$ = 460 ÷ 2
$\qquad\quad$ = **230**

5 = 10 ÷ 2

(b) $165 \times 5 = 165 \times 10 \div 2$
$= 1650 \div 2$
$= \mathbf{825}$

(c) **Method 1**

$38 \div 2 = 40 \div 2 - 2 \div 2$
$= 20 - 1$
$= \mathbf{19}$

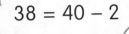
$38 = 40 - 2$

Method 2

$38 \div 2 = 30 \div 2 + 8 \div 2$
$= 15 + 4$
$= \mathbf{19}$

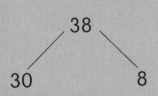

38
30   8

(d) $190 \div 5 = 190 \times 2 \div 5 \times 2$
$= 380 \div 10$
$= \mathbf{38}$

Multiply both numbers by 2.

Can you use other methods to perform these calculations mentally?

Answer all questions.

Do the following mentally.

1. 158 + 93 + 42

2. 997 + 605

3. 74 + 37 + 49

4. 234 + 567

5. 7000 − 137

6. 10,000 − 894

7. 126 − 75

8. 163 − 92

9. 58×2

10. 750×2

11. $92 \div 2$

12. $740 \div 2$

13. 85×5

14. 462×5

15. $620 \div 5$

16. $905 \div 5$

4 Bar Graphs

Worked Example 1

The bar graph below shows the number of animals sold by a pet shop in one month.

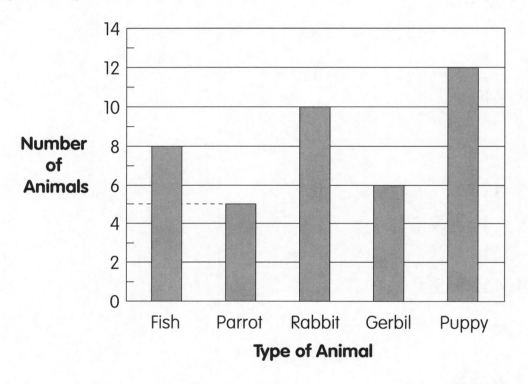

(a) How many parrots were sold during the month?
(b) How many more puppies than fishes were sold?
(c) How many fewer gerbils than rabbits were sold?

(a)

Number of Animals

14
12
10
8
6
5
4
2
0

Fish   Parrot   Rabbit   Gerbil   Puppy

Type of Animal

From the bar graph, the shop sold **5** parrots.

(b) From the bar graph, the pet shop sold 8 fishes and 12 puppies.

12 − 8 = 4

The shop sold **4** more puppies than fishes.

(c) From the bar graph, the pet shop sold 6 gerbils and 10 rabbits.

10 − 6 = 4

The shop sold **4** fewer gerbils than rabbits.

Worked Example 2

The bar graph below shows the number of stamps collected by five children.

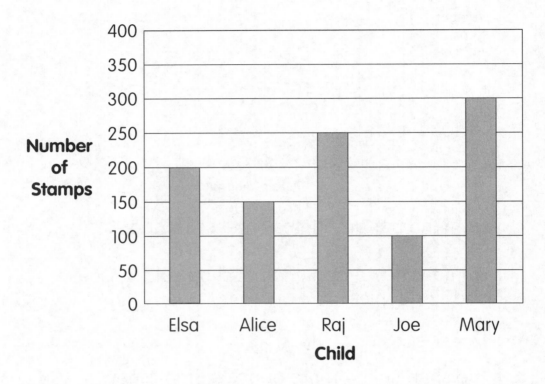

(a) How many more stamps does Raj have than Joe?

(b) How many fewer stamps does Alice have than Mary?

(c) How many stamps do Elsa, Mary and Raj have altogether?

(a) From the bar graph, Raj has 250 stamps and Joe has 100 stamps.

250 − 100 = 150

Raj has **150** more stamps than Joe.

(b) From the bar graph, Alice has 150 stamps and Mary has 300 stamps.

300 − 150 = 150

Alice has **150** fewer stamps than Mary.

(c) Elsa has 200 stamps, Mary has 300 stamps and Raj has 250 stamps.

200 + 300 + 250 = 750

Elsa, Mary and Raj have **750** stamps altogether.

Worked Example 3

The bar graph below shows the number of computers sold by a computer shop in a week.

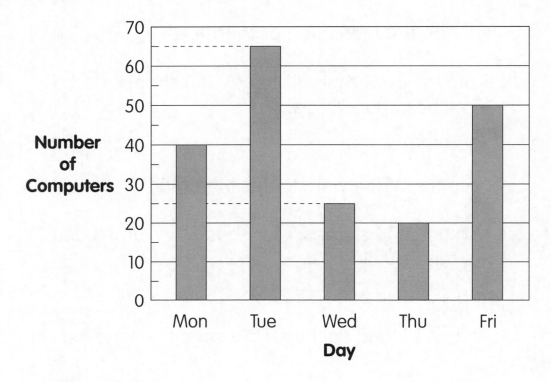

(a) How many more computers were sold on Tuesday than on Thursday?

(b) How many fewer computers were sold on Wednesday than on Monday?

(c) How many computers were sold during the week?

(a) From the bar graph, the shop sold 65 computers on Tuesday and 20 computers on Thursday.

65 – 20 = 45

45 more computers were sold on Tuesday than on Thursday.

(b) From the bar graph, the shop sold 40 computers on Monday and 25 computers on Wednesday.

40 – 25 = 15

15 fewer computers were sold on Wednesday than on Monday.

(c)

Day	Number of Computers
Monday	40
Tuesday	65
Wednesday	25
Thursday	20
Friday	50

40 + 65 + 25 + 20 + 50 = 200

200 computers were sold during the week.

Answer all questions. Show your work and write your statements clearly.

1. The bar graph below shows the favorite subject of each student in a class.

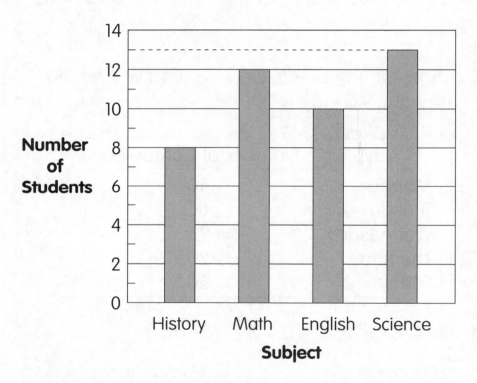

(a) Which is the most popular subject?

(b) How many more students prefer English to history?

(c) What is the total number of students in the class?

2. A group of students were asked to name their favorite color.

   The total number of students who liked red, blue and green was five times as many as those who liked purple.

   Complete the bar graph below.

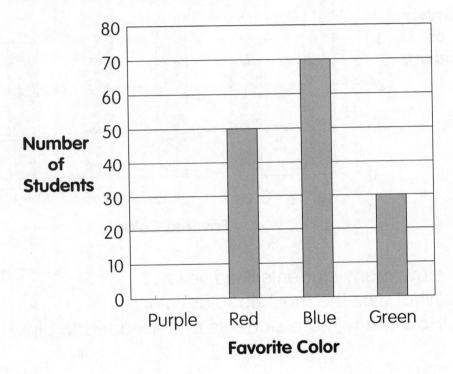

3. A group of students were asked to state their favorite color. The bar graph below summarizes the results.

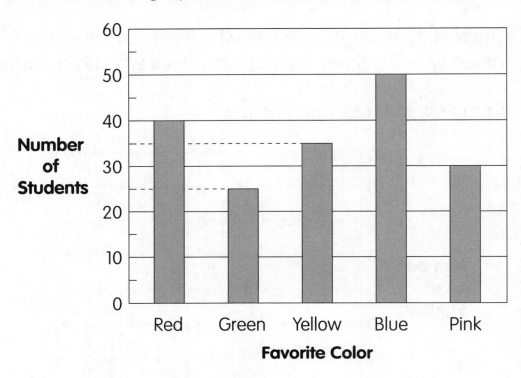

(a) How many students liked yellow?
(b) What was the most popular color?
(c) How many more students preferred red to pink?

4. A survey was conducted among 230 students on their favorite sport. The bar graph below shows the results.

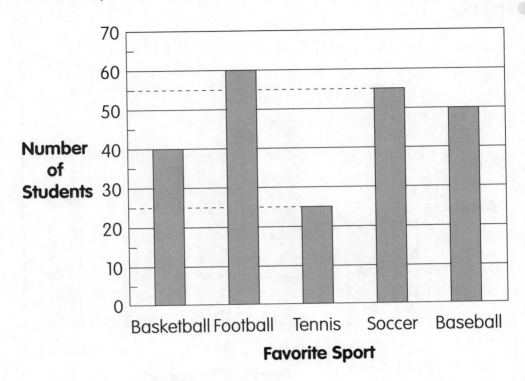

(a) Which sport was the least popular?
(b) How many students liked soccer?
(c) How many students chose football or baseball as their favorite sport altogether?

5. A group of adults were asked to name their preferred mode of transport. The bar graph below shows the results.

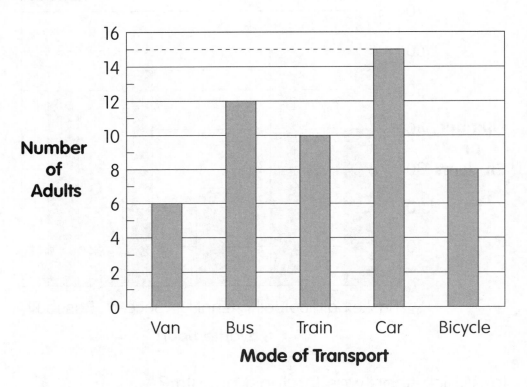

(a) How many adults preferred to travel by bus, car or van in all?

(b) There were as many adults who travelled by van and by bus as those who travelled by _____ and by
_____.

(c) How many more adults travelled by car than by bicycle?

(d) What is the difference between the number of adults who chose the most popular and the least popular mode of transport?

6. The bar graph below shows the hobbies of teenagers in a town.

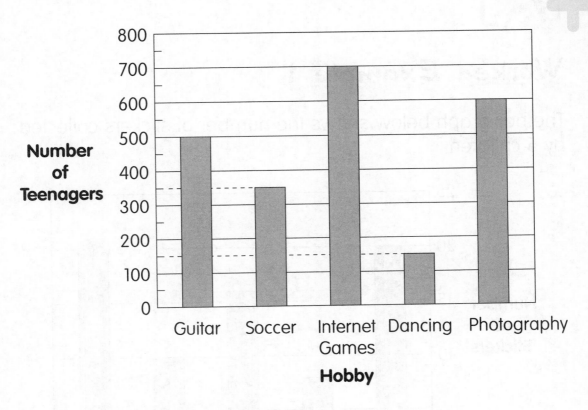

(a) What is the most popular hobby?
(b) How many teenagers like to play guitar?
(c) How many more teenagers prefer photography to dancing?
(d) How many teenagers like soccer or dancing altogether?
(e) How many fewer teenagers like dancing than internet games?

Worked Example 1

The bar graph below shows the number of stickers collected by 5 children.

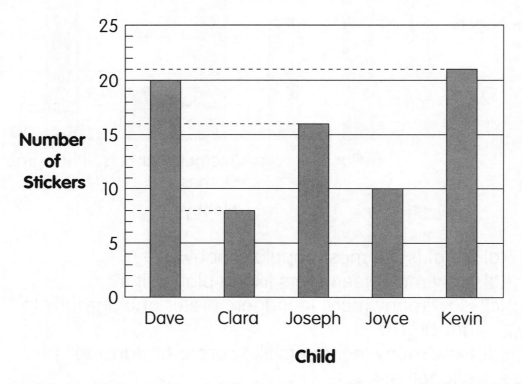

(a) How many more stickers does Joseph have than Clara?
(b) Who has twice as many stickers as Joyce?
(c) Who has half as many stickers as Joseph?
(d) What is the difference between the most number of stickers collected and the least number of stickers collected?
(e) All five children decide to share their stickers equally. How many stickers will each have after sharing?

(a) From the bar graph, Joseph has 16 stickers and Clara has 8 stickers.

16 − 8 = 8

Joseph has **8** more stickers than Clara.

(b) From the bar graph, Joyce has 10 stickers.

10 × 2 = 20

From the bar graph, Dave has 20 stickers.

Dave has twice as many stickers as Joyce.

(c) From the bar graph, Joseph has 16 stickers and Clara has 8 stickers.

16 ÷ 2 = 8

Clara has half as many stickers as Joseph.

(d) From the bar graph, Kevin has the most number of stickers (21) and Clara has the least number of stickers (8).

21 − 8 = 13

The difference in the number of stickers collected is **13**.

(e)

Child	Number of Stickers
Dave	20
Clara	8
Joseph	16
Joyce	10
Kevin	21

$20 + 8 + 16 + 10 + 21 = 75$

$75 \div 5 = 15$

Each student will have **15** stickers after sharing.

Worked Example 2

A survey was carried out to find out the flavor of ice cream children like most. The bar graph below summarizes the results.

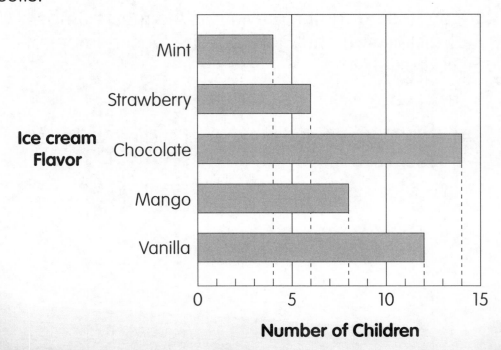

(a) How many children liked chocolate ice cream most?
(b) Which ice cream flavor was the least popular?
(c) Which ice cream flavor was twice as popular as strawberry flavor?
(d) How many fewer children preferred mango ice cream to vanilla ice cream?
(e) How many children took part in the survey?

(a)

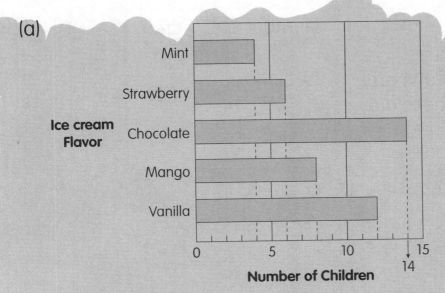

14 children liked chocolate ice cream most.

(b) From the bar graph, the shortest bar is the one representing mint ice cream.

Mint ice cream was the least popular.

(c) From the bar graph, 6 children liked strawberry ice cream.

$6 \times 2 = 12$

From the bar graph, 12 children liked vanilla ice cream.

Vanilla ice cream was twice as popular as strawberry ice cream.

(d) From the bar graph, 8 children liked mango ice cream and 12 children liked vanilla ice cream.

$12 - 8 = 4$

4 fewer children preferred mango ice cream to vanilla ice cream.

(e)

Flavor	Number of Children
Mint	4
Strawberry	6
Chocolate	14
Mango	8
Vanilla	12

$4 + 6 + 14 + 8 + 12 = 44$

44 children took part in the survey.

Answer all questions. Show your work and write your statements clearly.

1. The bar graph below shows the number of souvenirs distributed by a particular mathematics society in a week during its annual event.

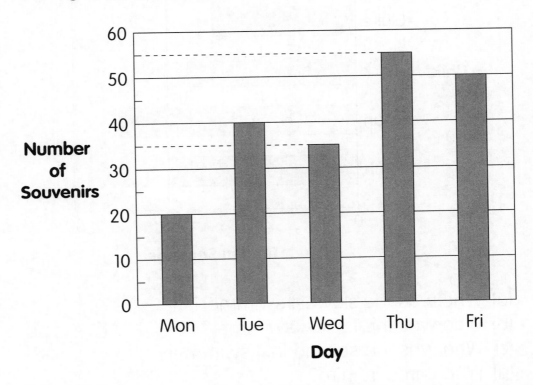

(a) How many souvenirs were distributed from Tuesday to Thursday?

(b) At the end of Friday, there were 15 souvenirs left. How many souvenirs did the mathematics society prepare for the week?

2. The bar graph below shows the times taken by five children to swim 50 meters.

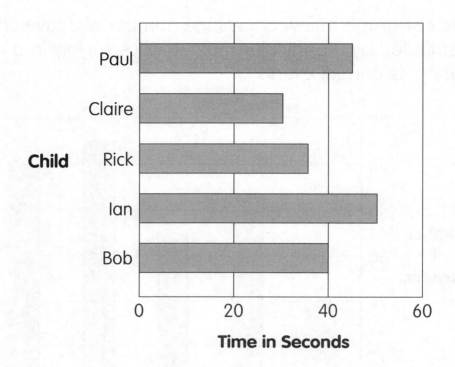

(a) Who was the slowest swimmer?
(b) Who was the fastest swimmer?
(c) Who was the second last swimmer?
(d) Who came in third?

3. The bar graph below shows the number of coins Rick collected from 2004 to 2008.

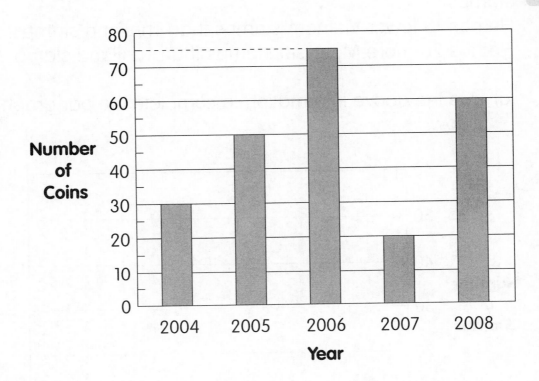

(a) Rick collected _____ times as many coins in 2008 as in 2007.

(b) Rick collected _____ fewer coins in 2004 and 2007 together than in 2006.

(c) 15 more coins were collected in _____ than in _____.

4. Arthur collects stamps from countries in Southeast Asia. He has 15 Brunei stamps and twice as many Thailand stamps.
He has 10 fewer Vietnam stamps than Thailand stamps.
He has 20 more Malaysia stamps than Thailand stamps.

(a) Use the above information to complete the bar graph below.

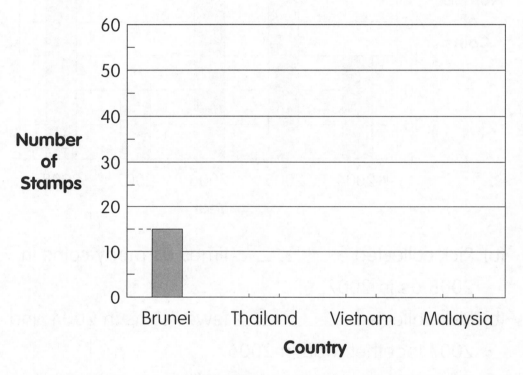

(b) Use the bar graph to answer these questions.

(i)   Arthur has the most number of _____ stamps.

(ii) He has the least number of _____ stamps.

(iii) Arthur has _____ more Malaysia stamps than Brunei stamps.

(iv) Arthur has _____ stamps altogether.

5. Ally is 11 years old.
   Cathy is 3 years younger than Ally.
   Helen is 5 years older than Cathy.
   Joanne is 3 years younger than Helen.

   (a) Use the above information to complete the bar graph
       below.

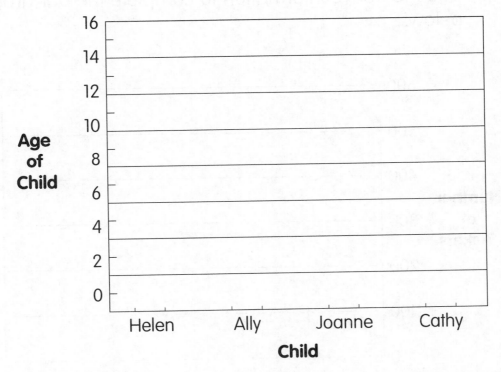

   (b) Use the bar graph to answer the following questions.
       (i)   What is the total age of Helen and Cathy?
       (ii) When Joanne reaches Helen's age, how old will
             Ally be?
       (iii) When Cathy reaches Joanne's age, how old will
             Helen be?

6. Aaron, Bob, Claire and Dave sold a total of 1000 concert tickets.

Claire sold as many tickets as the total number of tickets sold by Aaron and Bob.

Aaron sold half as many tickets as Bob.

Dave sold twice as many tickets as Bob.

(a) Use the above information to complete the bar graph below.

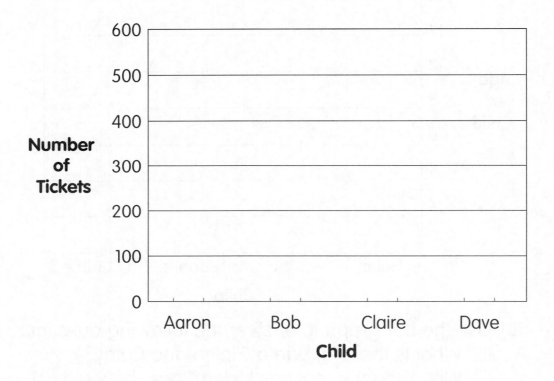

(b) Use the bar graph to answer these questions.
   (i)   Who sold the least number of tickets?
   (ii) Who sold the most number of tickets?
   (iii) How many more tickets would Bob have to sell in order to match the number of tickets sold by Claire?

 ⑤ Length

Worked Example 1

Sam and Jim have a total height of 3 m 27 cm. If Sam is 1 m 80 cm tall, how much taller is he than Jim?

1 m 80 cm

Sam

Jim

? 3 m 27 cm

3 m 27 cm − 1 m 80 cm = 1 m 47 cm

Jim is 1 m 47 cm.

1 m 80 cm − 1 m 47 cm = 33 cm

Sam is **33 cm** taller than Jim.

Worked Example 2

Dave and Joy have a total height of 8 ft 9 in. Joy and Rick have a total height of 8 ft 4 in. If Rick is 4 ft 6 in. tall, what is the height of Dave? Express your answer in feet and inches.

4 ft 6 in.

Rick

Joy

Dave

8 ft 4 in.

8 ft 9 in.

?

Method 1

8 ft 4 in. − 4 ft 6 in. = 3 ft 10 in.

Joy is 3 ft 10 in. tall.

8 ft 9 in. − 3 ft 10 in. = 4 ft 11 in.

Dave is **4 ft 11 in.** tall.

Method 2

4 ft 6 in. + 8 ft 9 in. = 13 ft 3 in.

The total height of Dave, Joy and Rick is **13 ft 3 in.**

13 ft 3 in. − 8 ft 4 in. = 4 ft 11 in.

Dave is **4 ft 11 in.** tall.

Worked Example 3

Town X and town Y are 4 km 225 m apart. Town Y and town Z are 3 km 550 m apart. Roy drove from town Z to town Y, then to town X. Finally, he drove back to town Y. What was the total distance Roy travelled in kilometers?

X ⟵——————⟶ Y ⟵——————— Z
　4 km 225 m　　　3 km 550 m

Journey	Distance travelled
From town Z to town Y	3 km 550 m
From town Y to town X	4 km 225 m
From town X to town Y	4 km 225 m

3 km 550 cm + 4 km 225 cm + 4 km 225 cm = 12 km

The total distance Roy travelled was **12 km.**

Answer all questions. Show your work and write your statements clearly.

1. Henry is 1 m 65 cm tall. Charles is 16 cm taller than Henry but 8 cm shorter than Albert. How tall is Albert? Give your answer in meters and centimeters.

2. Robin bought a string that is 3 m 25 cm long. He used 1 m 65 cm of the string to tie a box and another 1 m 25 cm to attach to a pebble. What length of string did he have left?

3. String P is twice as long as string Q. String R is three times as long as string P. Strings P, Q and R have a total length of 495 cm. What is the length of string R?

4. String A is twice as long as string B. String C is three times as long as string B. The total length of the three strings is 624 cm. What is the length (in meters and centimeters) of string A?

5. The total height of Lisa and Claire is 2 m 80 cm. The total height of Claire and Yvonne is 2 m 95 cm. If Yvonne's height is 1 m 45 cm, how tall is Lisa? Express your answer in meters and centimeters.

6. Adeline and Kelly have a total height of 10 ft 2 in. If Adeline is 5 ft 4 in. tall, find Kelly's height. Who is taller: Adeline or Kelly, and by how much?

7. The total length of string P and string Q is 818 cm. String P is 342 cm shorter than string Q. What is the length of string Q in meters and centimeters?

8. Farmer George planted 9 trees along one side of his farm. The distance between every two neighboring trees is 120 cm. What is the distance between the first tree and the last tree? Express your answer in meters and centimeters.

9. Two pieces of ribbon measure a total length of 938 cm. One ribbon is 280 cm longer than the other. What is the length of the longer ribbon in meters and centimeters?

10. The distance between bus stops B and C is three times the distance between bus stops A and B. The distance between bus stops B and C is 630 yd. What is the distance between bus stops A and C?

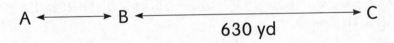

A ←——→ B ←——————————→ C
          630 yd

Worked Example 1

There are 30 trees along a straight road. Any two neighboring trees are 10 m apart. What is the distance between the third tree and the third last tree?

28 – 3 = 25 intervals

| 10 m | 10 m | 10 m | • • • | 10 m | 10 m |

3rd tree   4th tree   28th tree   29th tree   30th tree

3rd last tree

The interval between two neighboring trees is 10 m long. Between the 3rd tree and the third last tree (28th tree), there are 28 – 3 = 25 intervals between them.

25 intervals have a length of $25 \times 10 \text{ m} = 250 \text{ m}$

The distance between the third tree and the third last tree is **250 m**.

Worked Example 2

String P is twice as long as string Q. After 75 cm of string P is cut off, string P is half as long as string Q. What is the total length of both strings at first?

Before

String Q

String P

After

String Q

String P

75 cm

3 units   ⟶   75 cm

1 unit   ⟶   75 cm ÷ 3 = 25 cm

6 units   ⟶   6 × 25 cm = 150 cm

The total length of both strings at first is **150 cm**.

Answer all questions. Show your work and write your statements clearly.

1. A pink ribbon was twice as long as a white ribbon. When 2 m 30 cm of the pink ribbon was cut off, the remainder was still 3 m 40 cm longer than the white ribbon. How long was the pink ribbon at first? Express your answer in meters and centimeters.

2. There are 15 lamp posts along a stretch of road. The distance between 2 neighboring lamp posts is 500 m. What is the distance (in kilometers and meters) between the sixth and third last lamp posts?

3. Ribbon X was three times as long as ribbon Y. After 120 ft of ribbon X was cut off, ribbon X was twice as long as ribbon Y. What was the total length (in yards) of ribbons X and Y at first?

4. Bob is 5 ft 6 in. tall and Mark is 4 ft 7 in. tall. Their total height is 3 in. more than the total height of June and Anne. If June is 4 ft 9 in. tall, what is the height of Anne? Express your answer in feet and inches.

5. String A is 1 yd shorter than string B. String C is 1 ft 8 in. shorter than string B. The total length of the three strings is 13 ft 4 in. What is the length of string A?

6. A 5 m 70 cm white pole was 2 m 25 cm longer than a grey pole. When part of the white pole was cut off, it was 1 m 5 cm shorter than the grey pole. How much of the white pole was cut off? Express your answer in meters and centimeters.

7. Four rock-climbers have a length of rope each. Arthur and Bobby have 52 yd of rope altogether. Arthur and Dennis have 47 yd of rope in total. Dennis and Fred have a total of 62 yd of rope. What is the total length of rope Bobby and Fred have?

8. A piece of wire 480 cm long is bent to form a triangle of equal sides. What is the length of each side of the triangle in meters and centimeters?

9. String P is 42 cm longer than string Q. String R is 68 cm longer than string Q. The total length of strings P, Q and R is 320 cm. What is the total length of strings P and Q? Express your answer in meters and centimeters.

10. Stick A is 120 cm shorter than stick B. Stick C is 84 cm shorter than stick B. Sticks A, B and C have a total length of 360 cm. What is the total length (in meters and centimeters) of sticks A and C?

6 Weight

Worked Example 1

The total weight of a watermelon and a guava is 1 kg 700 g. The watermelon is 930 g heavier than the guava. How much do the guava and the watermelon each weigh?

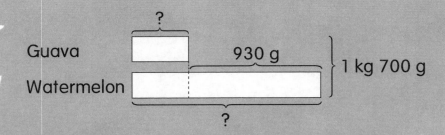

1 kg 700 g – 930 g = 770 g
770 g ÷ 2 = 385 g

The guava weighs is **385 g**.

385 g + 930 g = 1 kg 315 g

The watermelon weighs **1 kg 315 g**.

Worked Example 2

Crate Q weighs three times as much as crate P. Crate P weighs twice as much as crate R. If crate Q is 60 lb heavier than crate P, how much heavier is crate Q than crate R?

Crate P [ ][ ]   60 lb

Crate Q [ ][ ][ ][ ][ ][ ]

Crate R [ ]   ?

4 units ⟶ 60 lb

1 unit ⟶ 60 lb ÷ 4 = 15 lb

5 units ⟶ 5 × 15 lb = 75 lb

Crate Q is **75 lb** heavier than crate R.

Worked Example 3

Eve has 142 g of rice. Mary has 170 g of rice and Ian has 396 g of rice. What is the total weight of rice that Ian must give to Eve and Mary so that each of them has the same amount of rice?

142 g

Eve

Mary

170 g

Ian

396 g

142 g + 170 g + 396 g = 708 g

Eve, Mary and Ian have a total of 708 g of rice.

708 g ÷ 3 = 236 g

If the rice is divided equally among Eve, Mary and Ian, each of them will have 236 g of rice.

396 g − 236 g = 160 g

Ian must give **160 g** of rice to Eve and Mary so that each of them will have the same amount of rice.

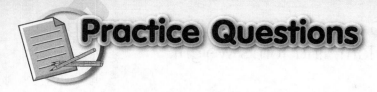

Practice Questions

Answer all questions. Show your work and write your statements clearly.

1. The total weight of a melon and a pear is 1 kg 550 g. The melon is 720 g heavier than the pear. What is the weight of the pear?

2. The total weight of a box of 9 apples is 3 lb. Each apple weighs 5 oz. What is the weight of the box?

3. Peter weighs 104 lb. Lisa is half as heavy as Peter. Timothy is 10 lb lighter than Lisa. How much does Timothy weigh?

4. The total weight of George and Tom is 248 lb. If George is 36 lb lighter than Tom, find Tom's weight.

5. The weight of a guava is 555 g. It is three times as heavy as an apple. What is the total weight of the guava and the apple?

6. Bag B weighs four times as much as bag A. Bag A weighs three times as much as bag C. If bag A is 180 g lighter than bag B, how much lighter is bag C than bag B?

7. Ten full crates of peanuts weigh 220 kg while an empty crate weighs 5 kg. What is the weight of the peanuts in each crate?

8. June has 456 g of flour, Ann has 210 g of flour and Joyce has 306 g of flour. How much flour must June give in total to Ann and Joyce in order that each of them has the same amount of flour?

9. The weight of Sue's bag is 20 lb 5 oz. The weight of Charlene's bag is 2 lb 10 oz lighter than Sue's bag. Keith's bag is 4 lb 6 oz heavier than Charlene's bag. What is the weight (in pounds and ounces) of Keith's bag?

10. A bag of onions weighs 7 kg. A bag of potatoes is
    4 kg 750 g lighter than the onions. A bag of grains is
    6 kg 25 g heavier than the potatoes.
    (a) What is the weight of the bag of potatoes?
    (b) What is the weight of the bag of grains?
    Express your answers in kilograms and grams.

11. Henry weighs 34 lb. His mother weighs 4 times as much
    as he does. His father weighs 26 lb more than his
    mother. Find his father's weight.

12. Box A is six times as heavy as box B. The total weight of
    the two boxes is 840 g. How much heavier is box A than
    box B?

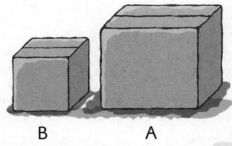

B   A

Challenging Problems

Worked Example 1

Albert, Paul and Jane have a total weight of 123 kg. Albert's weight is 32 kg. Paul weighs twice as much as Albert.
(a) What is Paul's weight?
(b) What is Jane's weight?

(a)

	32 kg
Albert	
Paul	

?

$32 \text{ kg} \times 2 = 64 \text{ kg}$

Paul's weight is **64 kg**.

(b)

32 kg

Albert

Paul

64 kg

Jane

?

123 kg

$32 \text{ kg} + 64 \text{ kg} = 96 \text{ kg}$

Albert and Paul weigh 96 kg altogether.

$123 \text{ kg} - 96 \text{ kg} = 27 \text{ kg}$

Jane's weight is **27 kg**.

Worked Example 2

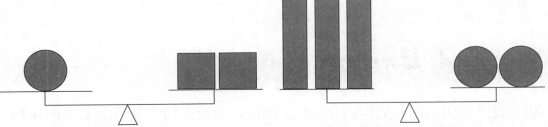

One circle balances
two squares.

Three rectangles balance
two circles.

Each circle weighs 90 g.
(a) How much does a square weigh?
(b) How much does a rectangle weigh?
(c) How many squares and rectangles will balance both
sides of the scales?

(a) 2 squares weigh 90 g.
1 square weighs 90 g ÷ 2 = **45 g**.

(b) 3 rectangles weigh as much as 2 circles.
3 rectangles weigh 2 × 90 g = 180 g.
1 rectangle weighs 180 g ÷ 3 = **60 g**.

(c)

Number of squares	Total weight (g)	Number of rectangles	Total weight (g)
1	45	1	60
2	90	2	120
3	135	3	(180)
4	(180)		

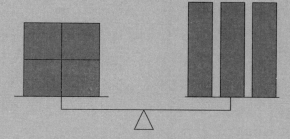

4 squares and **3 rectangles** will balance both sides of the scales.

Answer all questions. Show your work and write your statements clearly.

1. The weight of a pineapple is 880 g. The pineapple weighs 3 times more than an orange. What is the total weight of the pineapple and the orange? Express your answer in kilograms and grams.

2. In the figure below, what is the weight of X?

	50 g	20 g
50 g	X	100 g
200 g	200 g	500 g

200 g	100 g	20 g
200 g	200 g	500 g

3. Mrs. Yong buys the following items at the supermarket.

Item	Weight (g)
Fish	725 g
Cucumber	310 g
Carrots	275 g
Beef	1 kg 350 g
Watermelon	530 g
Cabbage	290 g

Express all your answers in kilograms and grams.
(a) What is the total weight of the lightest and the heaviest items?
(b) What is the total weight of all the items?
(c) If her son offers to help carry the meat, what is the total weight of the remaining items she needs to carry?

4. Bag A weighs 64 lb and bag B weighs 18 lb less than bag A. Bag C is twice as heavy as the total weight of bags A and B. What is the weight of bag C?

5. Box C is twice as heavy as box B. The weight of box A is two times more than the weight of box C. If box B weighs 90 g, what is the weight of box A?

6. The weight of item A is 1 kg 500 g. Item B is 310 g lighter than item A. Item C is 435 g less than item B.
   (a) What is the weight of item B?
   (b) What is the weight of item C?
   (c) What is the difference in weight between items A and C?

7. The total weight of Ann, Lisa and Karen is 101 kg. Lisa's weight is 56 kg. Ann weighs half as much as Lisa.
   (a) What is Ann's weight?
   (b) What is Karen's weight?

8.

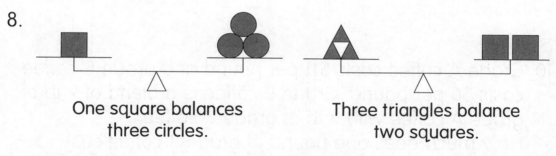

One square balances three circles.

Three triangles balance two squares.

How many circles and triangles will balance both sides of the scales?

9. The diagrams below show the weights of two similar
   bowls containing different numbers of identical marbles.
   (a) Find the weight of one marble.
   (b) Find the weight of one empty bowl.

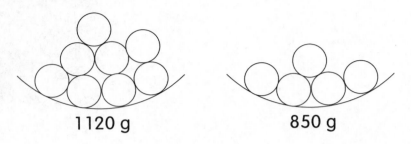

1120 g   850 g

10. Grade A coffee costs $11 per pound and grade C coffee
    costs $6 per pound. Grade B coffee is a blend of 2 lb of
    grade A coffee with 3 lb of grade C coffee.
    How much does one pound of grade B coffee cost?

 7 Capacity

Worked Example 1

A container has 625 ml of water. When 1 *l* 82 ml of water is poured into it, 107 ml of water overflows. What is the capacity of the container? Express your answer in liters and milliliters.

1 *l* 82 ml – 107 ml = 975 ml

975 ml of water is needed to fill the container.

625 ml + 975 ml = 1 *l* 600 ml

The capacity of the container is **1 *l* 600 ml**.

Worked Example 2

A tank is filled with 3 gal 3 qt of water. After 1 gal 1 qt of water is added into it, the tank is half filled. What is the capacity of the tank?

3 gal 3 qt + 1 gal 1 qt = 5 gal

Half the tank contains 5 gal of water.

The whole tank can hold 5 × 2 = 10 gal of water.

The capacity of the tank is **10 gal**.

What is the difference between capacity and volume?

Worked Example 3

A jug contains 2 _l_ 140 ml of orange juice. 1 _l_ 360 ml of the orange juice is poured into 2 bottles and the rest is poured equally into 3 cups. How much orange juice does each cup contain?

2 _l_ 140 ml – 1 _l_ 360 ml = 780 ml

780 ml of orange juice is poured equally into 3 cups.

780 ml ÷ 3 = 260 ml

Each cup contains **260 ml** of orange juice.

Answer all questions. Show your work and write your statements clearly.

1. A jug can hold 2 *l* 250 ml of water. A bottle can hold 1 *l* 340 ml less water than the jug. What is the total volume of water that both containers can hold? Express your answer in liters and milliliters.

2. A tank is filled to the brim with water. After 83 gal of water has been removed from it and another 29 gal added to it, the tank is half filled. What is the capacity of the tank?

3. An empty container has a capacity of 10 *l*. Paul adds 3 *l* 450 ml of water into it and Mary adds another 4 *l* 570 ml of water into it. How much more water can the container hold? Express your answer in liters and milliliters.

4. Jug A has 3 pt of water. Jug B has four times as much water as jug A but has 3 qt less water than jug C. What is the volume of water in jug C? Express your answer in gallons and quarts.

A   B   C

5. Oliver adds 370 ml of concentrated apple juice and 290 ml of concentrated pear syrup to 8 *l* 450 ml of water to make some punch for a party. How much punch does he make in all? Express your answer in liters and milliliters.

Apple juice   Pear juice

6. A pail had 3 *l* 485 ml of water. When 2 *l* 108 ml of water was poured into it, 93 ml of water overflowed. What is the capacity of the pail? Express your answer in liters and milliliters.

7. A jug can hold up to 1 gal 3 qt of water. Water from 12 full mugs, each of capacity 3 c, is poured into the jug. How much water will overflow?

8. Tom used the following types of juice to create his own concoction – *Fruit Juice Special*.

Juice	Amount (ml)
Carrot	220
Watermelon	1240
Mango	180
Pear	650

How much *Fruit Juice Special* was made? Express your answer in liters and milliliters.

9. Pot P can hold 725 ml of water. Pot Q can hold six times as much water as pot P. Pot R can hold 2 *l* 590 ml less water than pot Q. What is the capacity of pot R? Express your answer in liters and milliliters.

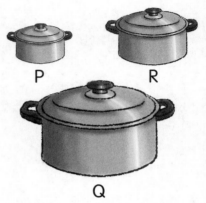

P   R

Q

10. Bucket A contains 440 ml of water. It contains half as much water as bucket B and twice as much water as bucket C. What is the total amount of water in buckets B and C? Express your answer in liters and milliliters.

Challenging Problems

Worked Example 1

Jill and Jack took turns to pour milk into a container. Jill used a 120 ml pail and Jack used a 150 ml pail. They stopped when they had poured the same volume of milk into the container.

(a) Find the number of times each had poured into the container.

(b) How much milk was poured into the container in all?

(a)

Jill: 120 ml

Number of times	Volume of milk
1	120
2	240
3	360
4	480
5	(600)

Jill poured **5** times.

Jack: 150 ml

Number of times	Volume of milk
1	150
2	300
3	450
4	(600)
5	750

Jack poured **4** times.

(b) 600 ml + 600 ml = 1 *l* 200 ml

1 *l* 200 ml milk was poured into the container in all.

Worked Example 2

One can and two bottles of *Koka Kola* have a total capacity of 410 ml. Two cans and one bottle of *Koka Kola* have a total capacity of 370 ml. Find the capacity of
(a) one can of *Koka Kola*,
(b) one bottle of *Koka Kola*.

Method 1

410 ml × 2 = 820 ml

| can | can | bottle | bottle | bottle | bottle |

?

370 ml

| can | can | bottle |

?

3 bottles ⟶ 820 ml − 370 ml = 450 ml
1 bottle ⟶ 450 ml ÷ 3 = 150 ml

2 cans ⟶ 370 ml − 150 ml = 220 ml
1 can ⟶ 220 ml ÷ 2 = 110 ml

(a) The capacity of one can of *Koka Kola* is **110 ml**.
(b) The capacity of one bottle of *Koka Kola* is **150 ml**.

Remember to check your answers!

Method 2

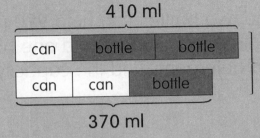

410 ml

410 ml + 370 ml = 780 ml

370 ml

780 ml ÷ 3 = 260 ml

1 can ⟶ 370 ml – 260 ml = 110 ml
1 bottle ⟶ 260 ml – 110 ml = 150 ml

(a) The capacity of one can of *Koka Kola* is **110 ml**.
(b) The capacity of one bottle of *Koka Kola* is **150 ml**.

Can you use another method to solve the problem?

Answer all questions. Show your work and write your statements clearly.

1. One plastic container and two bottles can hold 920 ml of liquid detergent. Two plastic containers and one bottle can hold 850 ml of liquid detergent. Find the capacity of
    (a) one plastic container,
    (b) one bottle.

2. Pails A and B have capacities of 3 l and 7 l respectively. Use these 2 pails to measure out
    (a) 1 liter of water,
    (b) 5 liters of water.

A   B

3. David and Ruth took turns to pour water into a pail.
   David used a 100-milliliter cup and Ruth used a 120-milliliter cup. They stopped when they had poured the
   same volume of water into the pail.
   (a) How many cups of water did each pour into the pail?
   (b) What was the total volume of water that was poured
       into the pail?

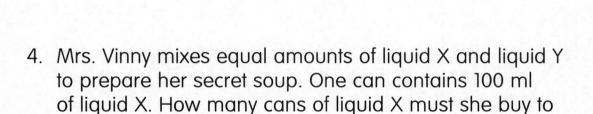

4. Mrs. Vinny mixes equal amounts of liquid X and liquid Y
   to prepare her secret soup. One can contains 100 ml
   of liquid X. How many cans of liquid X must she buy to
   prepare 2 *l* of soup?

5. Four jugs and four buckets can hold a total of 50 gal of water. Each jug can hold 2 qt of water. What is the capacity of 3 buckets?

6. Half a jug of water can fill exactly 5 glasses. Each glass has a capacity of 250 ml. Find the capacity of 4 jugs in liters.

7. Pails A, B and C have capacities of 3 l, 5 l and 8 l respectively. How can you use these 3 pails to measure out 4 l of water?

8. The total capacity of a pail and a jug is 10 *l*. The capacity of a pail is 9 *l* more than that of the jug. Find the capacity of the jug in milliliters.

9. Joel has a jar containing 220 ml of water. Elisa has a bigger jar that contains two times more water than Joel's jar. What is the total volume of water in both jars?

10. A big container has 12 *l* of water. Given 2 pails of capacities 5 *l* and 9 *l*, how can you divide the volume of water equally between the 9 *l* pail and the big container?

8 Money

Worked Example 1

Jeremy and Rita have $52.80 altogether. If Rita has $18.90, how much more money does Jeremy have than Rita?

$18.90

Rita

Jeremy

$52.80

?

$52.80 − $18.90 = $33.90

Jeremy has $33.90.

$33.90 − $18.90 = $15

Jeremy has **$15** more than Rita.

Worked Example 2

Mrs. Tan bought 9 muffins at 95¢ each. If she paid for the items with a $20 bill, how much change would she get?

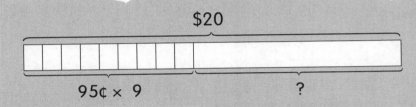

95¢ × 9 = 855¢
855¢ = $8.55

9 muffins cost $8.55.

95 = 100 − 5
95 × 9 = 100 × 9 − 5 × 9
= 855

$20.00 − $8.55 = $11.45

She would get **$11.45** change.

Worked Example 3

Joe and Ruth have $62.80 in total.
Joe has $18.80 more than Ruth.
How much money does each have?

Method 1

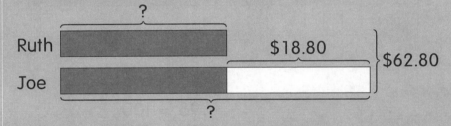

2 ▇ ———→ $62.80 − $18.80 = $44

1 ▇ ———→ $44 ÷ 2 = $22

$22 + $18.80 = $40.80

Ruth has **$22** and Joe has **$40.80**.

Method 2

Twice of Joe's money = $62.80 + $18.80
                     = $81.60

$81.60 ÷ 2 = $40.80
$40.80 − $18.80 = $22

Ruth has **$22** and Joe has **$40.80**.

Practice Questions

Answer all questions. Show your work and write your statements clearly.

1. Betty has $18.70, Cathy has $33.40 and Danny has $52.10. How much money do all three have in total?

2. Matthew bought a shirt for $22.90 and a pair of pants for $42.50. He paid for both items with a $100 bill. How much change did he receive?

3. Kelvin and Jack shared $28 equally. If Jack donated $5.60 to charity, how much money did he have left?

4. After buying five coloring books that cost $3 each, Mary had $8.50 left. How much money did she have at first?

5. The total savings of Jenny and Irene are $51.35. If Jenny saves $23.80, how much more money does Irene save than Jenny?

6. Joshua plans to buy a basketball costing $27.35. His godfather gives him five $5 bills. How much more money does he need?

7. Jim and Justin have the same amount of money at first. Jim receives $12.50 from his father while Justin gives $12.50 to his sister. How much more money does Jim have than Justin now?

8. Jennifer has $35. She plans to save $5 a week to buy a dress that costs $95. How many weeks must she save before she can buy the dress?

9. Roy and June have $137 altogether. June has $29 more than Roy. How much money does each have?

10. Tim had to mail the following packages:

   (a) Package 1 cost 42¢.
   (b) Package 2 cost 76¢.
   (c) Package 3 cost 94¢.

   He had 10¢, 22¢ and 50¢ stamps to make up the correct amount for each package. What stamps were used for each of the above packages?

11. Joseph and his three friends collected used bottles and took them to the recycling center. They collected $52, which they divided equally among themselves. How much did each boy get?

12. Andrew bought 10 erasers at 2 for 90¢. The erasers usually cost 50¢ each. How much did Andrew pay for the erasers?

Challenging Problems

Worked Example 1

Chris buys some cookies at 20¢ each. He then sells them for 25¢ each. How many cookies must he sell in order to earn $1.20?

He made 25¢ − 20¢ = 5¢ on every cookie he sells.

$1.20 = 120¢
120¢ ÷ 5¢ = 24

Chris must sell **24** cookies.

Worked Example 2

Samuel has four times as much money as Ben. If Samuel has $90 more than Ben, how much money do they have in all?

Ben

Samuel

?

$90

3 units ⟶ $90
1 unit ⟶ $90 ÷ 3 = $30
5 units ⟶ $30 × 5 = $150

They have **$150** in all.

Worked Example 3

One mango and one pear cost $3.30.
Two mangoes and five pears cost $9.00.
How much does one mango cost?

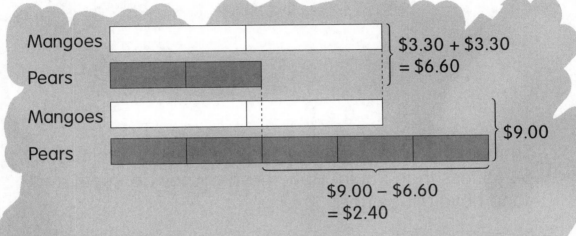

Mangoes

Pears

$3.30 + $3.30
= $6.60

Mangoes

Pears

$9.00

$9.00 − $6.60
= $2.40

3 pears cost $2.40.

$2.40 = 240¢
240¢ ÷ 3 = 80¢
80¢ = $0.80

1 pear costs $0.80.
2 pears cost $0.80 + $0.80 = $1.60.

2 mangoes + 2 pears ⟶ $6.60
2 mangoes + $1.60 ⟶ $6.60
2 mangoes ⟶ $6.60 − $1.60
= $5.00
1 mango ⟶ $2.50

Check:
5 pears ⟶ 5 × $0.80
= $4.00
2 mangoes + 5 pears
⟶ $5.00 + $4.00
= $9.00

One mango costs **$2.50**.

Answer all questions. Show your work and write your statements clearly.

1. Jonathan buys some fish for 20¢ each. He then sells them for 25¢ each. How many fish must he sell in order to earn 60¢?

2. Smith has $12.40. Jane has $3.50 more than Smith but $4.65 less than Robin. How much money do Robin and Jane have altogether?

3. Mr. Tan sells apples at 40¢ each. Mr. Yang sells five apples for $1.80. If you are buying five apples, who should you buy from if you want to spend less money? Why?

4. Ashley has four times as much money as Dave. If Ashley has $180 more than Dave, how much money do they have in total?

5. A vending machine has yellow balls, green balls and blue balls. Each ball costs $1. The balls fall into a bag you cannot see into. What is the least amount of money that you need to spend to be sure there are 2 balls of the same color in the bag?

6. Anne has three times as much money as Eve. If Eve has $70 less than Anne, how much money do they have altogether?

7. In total, Adam and Pam have $58.10. Pam has $9.90 more than Adam. How much does each have?

8. A dealer pays $15.30 for 9 badges. He sells each badge for $2. How much profit does he make on each badge?

9. Joseph collected 705 commemorative quarters. Louis collected 158 more quarters than Joseph. How many quarters did they collect altogether?

10. One orange and one apple cost $1.05. Two oranges and three apples cost $2.75. How much do two apples cost?

11. Henry bought two items. He paid with a $20 bill and got $2.40 change. Which items did he buy from the list below?

Item	Price
T-shirt	$7.90
Shorts	$9.50
Socks	$5.70
Jacket	$8.10
Shoes	$12.90

12. One pear and two oranges cost $1.00.
Two pears and one orange cost $1.10.
What is the total cost of two pears and two oranges?

9 Fractions

Worked Example 1

How many more triangles must be shaded so that $\frac{3}{4}$ of the figure is shaded?

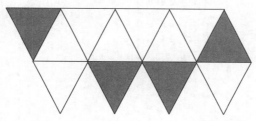

There are 12 triangles in the figure.

$$\frac{3}{4} = \frac{9}{12}$$

$\frac{3}{4}$ of the figure is made up of 9 triangles.

Only 4 triangles are shaded.

$$9 - 4 = 5$$

5 more triangles must be shaded so that $\frac{3}{4}$ of the figure is shaded.

Worked Example 2

Arrange the following fractions in order, beginning with the greatest.

$$\frac{1}{4} \quad \frac{1}{5} \quad \frac{7}{8} \quad \frac{1}{2}$$

$$\frac{1}{4} = \frac{2}{8} \qquad \frac{1}{4} = \frac{5}{20}$$

$$\frac{1}{2} = \frac{4}{8} \qquad \frac{1}{5} = \frac{4}{20} \left.\right\} \quad \frac{1}{4} \text{ is greater than } \frac{1}{5}$$

$$\frac{7}{8}$$

Beginning with the greatest, we have

$$\frac{7}{8} \quad \frac{1}{2} \quad \frac{1}{4} \quad \frac{1}{5}$$

Worked Example 3

Terrence cut a cake into 6 equal pieces and ate 2 pieces. Jane cut the remaining cake into 8 equal pieces and took 3 pieces. What fraction of the cake was left?

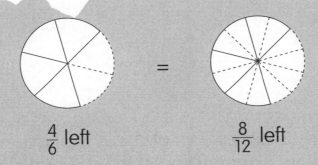

$\dfrac{4}{6}$ left $\dfrac{8}{12}$ left

After Terrence cut the cake, fraction of the cake left

$= \dfrac{4}{6} = \dfrac{8}{12}$

Each piece of the remaining cake represents $\dfrac{1}{12}$ of the cake.

Three pieces of the remaining cake represent $\dfrac{3}{12}$ of the cake.

After Jane took 3 pieces of cake, fraction of the cake left

$= \dfrac{8}{12} - \dfrac{3}{12}$

$= \dfrac{5}{12}$

$\dfrac{5}{12}$ of the cake was left.

Answer all questions. Show your work and write your statements clearly.

1. James had 12 marbles. He lost 3 of them. What fraction of the marbles was left? Express your answer in its simplest form.

2. Robert won 18 stuffed toys at a fair. He gave 6 stuffed toys to charity. What fraction of the stuffed toys was left? Express your answer in its simplest form.

3. How many quarters are there in 9 wholes?

4. The figure below is made up of 12 identical rectangles. What fraction of the figure is shaded?

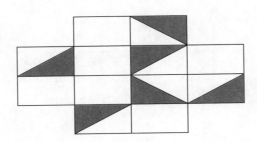

5. Given that $\frac{6}{9} = \frac{4}{\boxed{}}$, what number does $\boxed{}$ stand for?

6. Shade $\frac{3}{5}$ of the figure below.

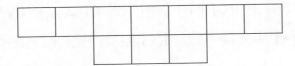

7. Arrange the following fractions in order, beginning with the smallest.

$$\frac{1}{2} \quad \frac{5}{6} \quad \frac{3}{4}$$

8. How many more rectangles must be shaded so that $\frac{5}{6}$ of the figure is shaded?

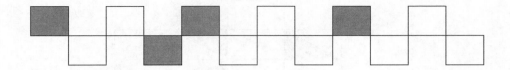

9. Arrange the following fractions in order, beginning with the greatest.

$$\frac{1}{3} \quad \frac{5}{6} \quad \frac{3}{4}$$

10. Alice spent $\frac{1}{4}$ h ironing clothes and $\frac{3}{4}$ h washing dishes. How long did she take to finish her chores?

Challenging Problems

Worked Example 1

Joe used the following pattern blocks to make fraction sentences in (a) pictures, (b) words, (c) numbers.

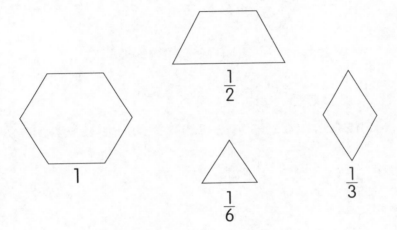

For example,

(a) 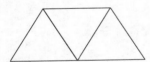   is the same as

(b) Three sixths is the same as one half.

(c) $\frac{3}{6} = \frac{1}{2}$

Using the pattern blocks, write all possible fraction sentences for the number 1.

127

1. (a)  is the same as

(b) **Two halves is the same as one whole.**

(c) $\frac{2}{2} = 1$

2. (a) 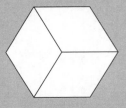 is the same as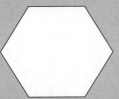

(b) **Three thirds is the same as one whole.**

(c) $\frac{3}{3} = 1$

3. (a) 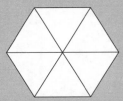 is the same as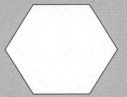

(b) **Six sixths is the same as one whole.**

(c) $\frac{6}{6} = 1$

Worked Example 2

Sam gave $\frac{1}{7}$ of his stamps to Ann. He gave $\frac{1}{3}$ of what was left to Mary, and the remaining stamps to Susan.
(a) What fraction of Sam's stamps were given to Mary?
(b) What fraction of Sam's stamps were given to Susan?

Let the number of stamps Sam had be divided into 7 equal parts.

```
┌────┬────┬────┬────┬────┬────┬────┐
│████│    │    │    │    │    │    │
└────┴────┴────┴────┴────┴────┴────┘
  └─┘
  Ann
```

After Sam had given $\frac{1}{7}$ of his stamps to Ann, there were 6 parts left.

$\frac{1}{3} = \frac{2}{6}$

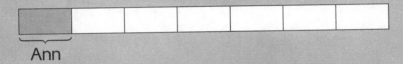

Ann   Mary   Susan

Out of 6 parts, Sam gave 2 parts to Mary and the remaining 4 parts to Susan.

(a) Mary received 2 out of 7 parts. $\frac{2}{7}$ of Sam's stamps were given to Mary.

(b) Susan received 4 out of 7 parts. $\frac{4}{7}$ of Sam's stamps were given to Susan.

Answer all questions. Show your work and write your statements clearly.

1. Using as many of the pattern blocks below, form fraction sentences for equivalent fractions in (a) pictures, (b) words, (c) numbers.

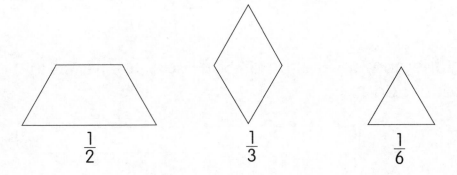

$$\frac{1}{2} \qquad \frac{1}{3} \qquad \frac{1}{6}$$

2. Study the figures below and fill in the missing numbers.

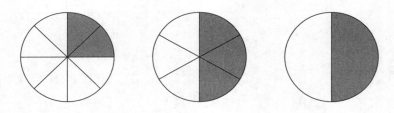

(a) $\dfrac{1}{\Box} + \dfrac{1}{\Box} = \dfrac{1}{4}$

(b) $\dfrac{1}{\Box} + \dfrac{1}{\Box} + \dfrac{1}{\Box} = \dfrac{1}{2}$

3. If 18 represents half of the circle below, what number is represented by the shaded part of the circle?

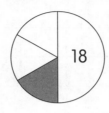

4. Study the figures below. Fill in the missing numbers given that they are the same.

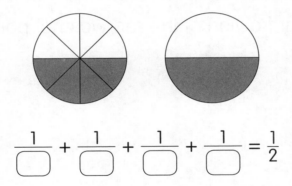

$$\frac{1}{\bigcirc} + \frac{1}{\bigcirc} + \frac{1}{\bigcirc} + \frac{1}{\bigcirc} = \frac{1}{2}$$

5. (a) With the help of the diagram below, find a pair of fractions such that their sum is $\frac{7}{10}$.

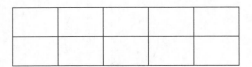

(b) With the help of the diagram below, find a pair of fractions such that one fraction is $\frac{3}{10}$ more than the other.

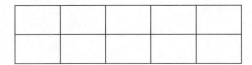

6. Richard painted $\frac{1}{5}$ of a rod blue and $\frac{1}{4}$ of the remainder green. What fraction of the rod was not painted?

7. Mrs. Yan had one meter of string. She used $\frac{5}{10}$ m of it to tie a box and another $\frac{3}{10}$ m to make a pendulum. What length of string was left?

8. Fiona cut a cake into 5 equal pieces and ate 2 pieces. Ian cut the remaining cake into 6 equal pieces and took 3 pieces. What fraction of the cake was left?

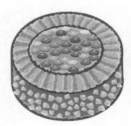

9. Oliver gave $\frac{1}{9}$ of his stickers to Mark. He then gave $\frac{1}{4}$ of the remaining stickers to Paul and the rest to Karen.
   (a) What fraction of Oliver's stickers was given to Paul?
   (b) What fraction of Oliver's stickers was given to Karen?

10. Mr. Torres gave $\frac{1}{10}$ of his money to the church. He also gave $\frac{2}{3}$ of his remaining money to his wife and children. He then saved the rest.
    (a) What fraction of his money did he give to his family members?
    (b) What fraction of his money did he save?

10 Time

Worked Example 1

How many minutes are there between 10:35 p.m. on Saturday and 1:27 a.m. the next day?

10:35 p.m. $\xrightarrow{\text{2 h}}$ 12:35 a.m. $\xrightarrow{\text{25 min}}$ 1:00 a.m.

$\downarrow$ 27 min

1:27 a.m.

2 h = 2 × 60
    = 120 min

120 min + 25 min + 27 min = 172 min

There are **172** minutes between 10:35 p.m. on Saturday and 1:27 a.m. the next day.

Worked Example 2

Ivan took 1 h 32 min to learn how to fold a paper rat. He took 47 min more to learn how to fold a paper rabbit than that taken to fold the paper rat. How long did he take to learn how to fold the paper rat and paper rabbit?

1 h 32 min

Paper rat

Paper rabbit

?

47 min

1 h 32 min + 47 min = 1 h 79 min
= 2 h 19 min

Ivan took 2 h 19 min to learn how to fold the paper rabbit.

1 h 32 min + 2 h 19 min = 3 h 51 min

He took **3 h 51 min** to learn how to fold the paper rat and paper rabbit.

Worked Example 3

Jeremy took 7 h 20 min to work out ten challenging problems. Rashid solved the same questions 45 minutes faster than Jeremy. Both of them started working on the problems at 1:30 p.m.

(a) How long did Rashid take to solve all ten problems?

(b) At what time did Rashid finish solving the questions?

(a) 45 min = 20 min + 25 min

$$7 \text{ h } 20 \text{ min} \xrightarrow{-20 \text{ min}} 7 \text{ h} \xrightarrow{-25 \text{ min}} 6 \text{ h } 35 \text{ min}$$

Rashid took **6 h 35 min** to solve all ten problems.

(b)

$$1:30 \text{ p.m.} \xrightarrow{+6 \text{ h}} 7:30 \text{ p.m.} \xrightarrow{+35 \text{ min}} 8:05 \text{ p.m.}$$

Rashid finished solving the questions at **8:05 p.m.**

Practice Questions

Answer all questions. Show your work and write your statements clearly.

1. A movie started at 8:15 p.m. and ended at 10:00 p.m. How long did the movie last?

2. Mrs. Aguilar began her lesson at 11:35 a.m. and finished at 12:15 p.m. How long was she teaching?

3. An amusement park is open from 8:30 a.m. to 6:00 p.m. every day except on Sundays. How long are the opening hours for each day?

4. A movie ended at 8:15 p.m. It lasted for 80 minutes. At what time did it start?

5. Yesterday was Monday. What day is 4 days after tomorrow?

6. How many minutes are there between 9:40 p.m. on Sunday and 2:15 a.m. the next day?

7. A soccer match starts at 5:00 p.m. Each half of the match lasts 45 minutes and there is a 10-minute break at half time. At what time will the soccer match end?

8. How many minutes are there between 9:25 p.m. on Thursday and 1:19 a.m. the next day?

9. Arthur and David spent a total of 9 h 18 min to complete a project. If Arthur spent 5 h 25 min on the project, how much longer did he take than David?

10. Henry took 1 h 26 min to build a toy castle. He took 32 min more to build a toy castle than to build a toy house. How long did he take to build a toy castle and a toy house altogether?

11. Jennifer and Ian spent a total of 32 minutes jogging round their neighborhood. Jennifer took 4 minutes more than Ian. How long did Jennifer jog?

12. How many days are there from 18 May to 17 June inclusive?

Challenging Problems

Worked Example 1

Bus service 28 leaves the terminal every 10 minutes. Bus service 111 leaves the same terminal every 15 minutes. On Sunday, both services leave the terminal at 9:00 a.m. When will both services next leave the terminal together?

Time of departure	
Bus service 28	Bus service 111
9:00 a.m.	9:00 a.m.
9:10 a.m.	9:15 a.m.
9:20 a.m.	9:30 a.m.
9:30 a.m.	9:45 a.m.

Both services will next leave the terminal together at **9:30 a.m.**

Worked Example 2

A train service runs every 15 minutes. If there is a train at 7:25 a.m., how many trains are there between 6:00 a.m. and 9:00 a.m. altogether?

Time	
6:10 a.m.	7:40 a.m.
6:25 a.m.	7:55 a.m.
6:40 a.m.	8:10 a.m.
6:55 a.m.	8:25 a.m.
7:10 a.m.	8:40 a.m.
7:25 a.m.	8:55 a.m.

There are trains before and after 7:25 a.m. at 15 min interval.

There are **12** trains between 6:00 a.m. and 9:00 a.m. altogether.

Worked Example 3

Yesterday was Tuesday. What day is 3 days before 4 days after tomorrow?

Step 1: Yesterday was Tuesday.

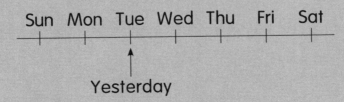

Step 2: Today is Wednesday.

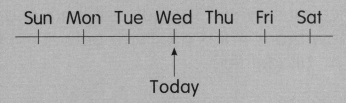

Step 3: Tomorrow is Thursday.

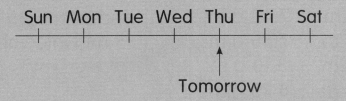

Step 4: 4 days after tomorrow.

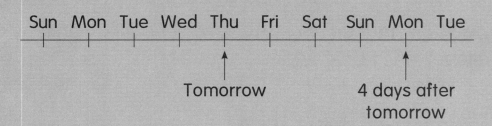

Step 5: 3 days before 4 days after tomorrow.

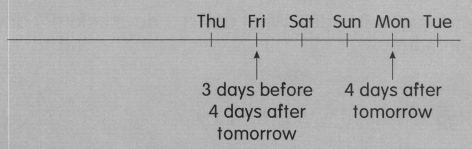

3 days before 4 days after tomorrow is a **Friday**.

Answer all questions. Show your work and write your statements clearly.

1. Bus service 24 leaves the interchange every 6 minutes. Bus service 79 leaves the same interchange every 8 minutes. On Sunday, both services leave the interchange at 7:00 p.m. When will both services next leave the interchange together?

2. Joyce made two dinosaurs out of clay. She took 3 h 35 min to make the first dinosaur. She took 2 h 50 min to make the second dinosaur. She finished making both dinosaurs at 4:05 p.m.
   (a) How long did she take to make both dinosaurs?
   (b) At what time did she start working on the dinosaurs?

3. Tomorrow is Sunday. What day is 3 days after 3 days before yesterday?

4. A carpenter takes 60 minutes to saw a piece of wood into six pieces. How long will it take him to saw an identical piece of wood into eleven pieces?

5. A clock loses 5 minutes every hour. The clock is adjusted to the correct time at 8:00 a.m. on Sunday. What time will it show at 8:00 a.m. on the following Monday?

6. (a) On what dates of a month is the sum of the digits equal to 4?
   (b) What are the least and most number of times these dates will occur in a month?

7. A bus service runs every 15 minutes. If there is a bus at 9:20 a.m., how many buses are there between 8:00 a.m. and 11:00 a.m. altogether?

8. Tom has a habit of adjusting his watch every hour, by making it run 5 minutes faster than usual. If he first adjusts his watch at 5 p.m., what is the correct time when his watch shows 9 p.m.?

9. Sally is 12 years old. The digits of her age can be switched to obtain her cousin's age. In the near future, their ages can be obtained by switching the digits of their ages again. In how many years' time will this happen again? (Hint: Draw a table and find their ages each year.)

10. How many minutes are there between 9:25 p.m. on Wednesday and 1:19 a.m. on Friday?

11. Perry and Celeste took a total of 14 minutes 26 seconds to cycle round a few apartments. Perry took 3 minutes 38 seconds less than Celeste. How long (in minutes and seconds) did Celeste cycle? (One minute = 60 seconds)

12. The clocks show the times in three cities at the same time.

Geneva
Sun, 6:30 a.m.

Singapore
Sun, 1:30 p.m.

Sydney
Sun, 4:30 p.m.

(a) What is the time difference between Geneva and Singapore?

(b) What is the time difference between Singapore and Sydney?

(c) If it is 6:10 a.m. in Singapore, what is the time in Geneva?

(d) If it is 10:25 a.m. in Sydney, what is the time in Singapore?

11 Angles

Worked Example 1

In the figure below, how many angles are there?

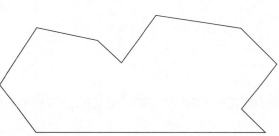

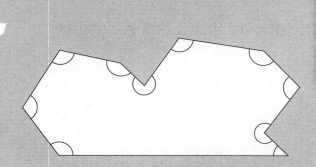

In closed figures, only consider the internal angles.

There are **10** angles.

Worked Example 2

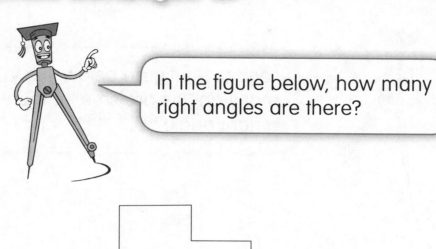

In the figure below, how many right angles are there?

Only consider inside angles.

There are **6** right angles.

Worked Example 3

Look at the figure below. How many angles are smaller than a right angle?

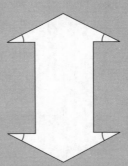

There are **4** angles smaller than a right angle.

Practice Questions

Answer all questions. Show your work and write your statements clearly.

1. In the figure below, how many right angles are there?

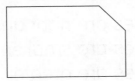

2. In the figure below, find the number of angles that are
   (a) smaller than a right angle,
   (b) greater than a right angle.

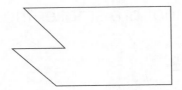

3. Study these angles and complete the table below.

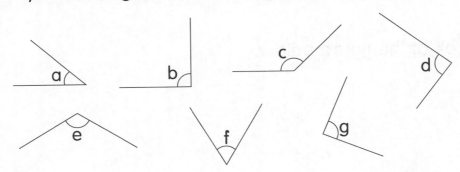

	Angle
Right angle	
Smaller than a right angle	
Greater than a right angle	

4. Look at the figure below.

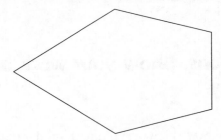

(a) How many angles are right angles?
(b) How many angles are smaller than a right angle?
(c) How many angles are greater than a right angle?

5. Mark the angles that are smaller than a right angle.

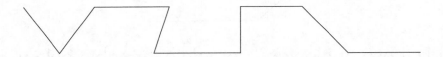

6. Look at the figure below.

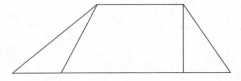

(a) How many angles are right angles?
(b) How many angles are smaller than a right angle?

7. Study the figure below and answer the following questions.

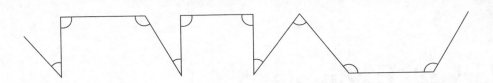

    (a) How many angles are right angles?
    (b) How many angles are greater than a right angle?

8. What is the greatest number of right angles that a four-sided figure can have?

9. Look at the figures below. Which figure has each of its angles greater than a right angle?

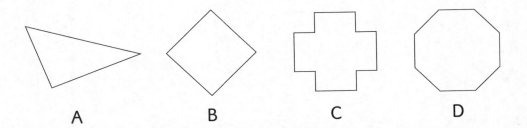

    A   B   C   D

10. In the figure below, how many angles are greater than a right angle?

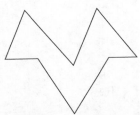

Challenging Problems

Worked Example 1

Which angle is bigger?

They are the **same**, although the left angle appears to be bigger than the right angle due to the lengths of the lines that form their angles.

Worked Example 2

In the figure below, how many right angles are there?

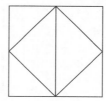

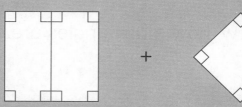

8 + 4 = 12

There are **12** right angles.

Answer all questions. Show your work and write your statements clearly.

1. Study the figures below and answer the following questions.

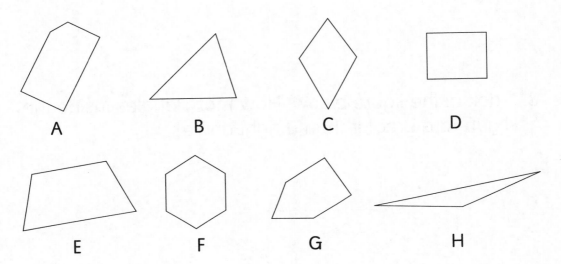

A   B   C   D

E   F   G   H

(a) Name two figures that have at least one right angle each.

(b) Name three figures that have at least one angle greater than a right angle.

(c) Name a figure with each of its angles smaller than a right angle.

(d) Name a figure with each of its angles greater than a right angle.

2. Which angle is smaller?

3. Look at the figure below. How many angles inside the figure are greater than a right angle?

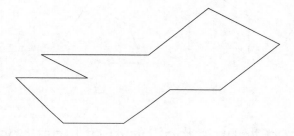

4. What is the greatest number of right angles that a six-sided figure can have? (A six-sided figure is a figure with 6 sides.)

5. In each of the following diagrams, how many right angles are there?

(a)

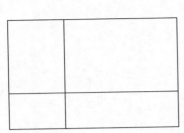

(b)

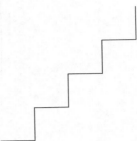

6. In the figure below, how many right angles are there?

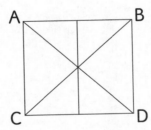

7. How many angles smaller than a right angle can be formed from this figure?

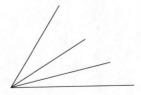

8. In the figure below, how many right angles are there?

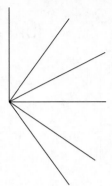

9. (a) Draw an angle that is greater than a right angle.
   (b) Draw an angle that is smaller than a right angle.

10. Fold a paper circle in half and then in half again. What fraction of a turn is a right angle?

12 Perimeter and Area

Worked Example 1

The figure shows a rectangular farm land. What is its perimeter?

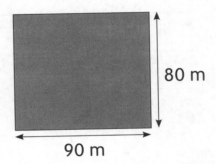

80 m

90 m

Perimeter = length + width + length + width
= 90 m + 80 m + 90 m + 80 m
= 340 m

Its perimeter is **340 m**.

Another way to find perimeter is:
90 + 80 = 170
170 × 2 = 340

Worked Example 2

A rectangular painting is twice as long as it is wide. It is 60 cm long. What is its perimeter?

60 cm

Length

Width

$60 \text{ cm} \div 2 = 30 \text{ cm}$

Its width is 30 cm.

Perimeter = length + width + length + width
$$= 60 \text{ cm} + 30 \text{ cm} + 60 \text{ cm} + 30 \text{ cm}$$
$$= 180 \text{ cm}$$

Its perimeter is **180 cm**.

Drawing a model helps us to visualise the situation better.

Worked Example 3

What is the perimeter and area of each figure?

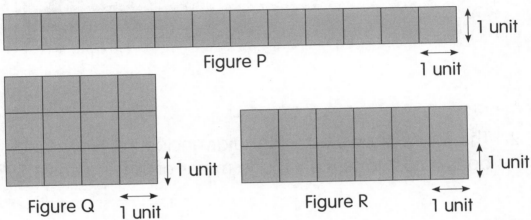

Figure P

1 unit

1 unit

Figure Q   1 unit   1 unit

Figure R   1 unit   1 unit

Perimeter of figure P = **26 units**
Perimeter of figure Q = **14 units**
Perimeter of figure R = **16 units**

The area of one square is
1 square unit.

By counting the squares in
each figure,

These figures have the
same area but different
perimeters.

area of figure P = **12 square units**
area of figure Q = **12 square units**
area of figure R = **12 square units**

Answer all questions. Show your work and write your statements clearly.

1. The figure below shows a rectangular strip of paper. Find its perimeter.

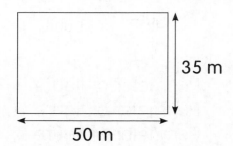

6 cm

18 cm

2. The figure shows a rectangular enclosure. How much does it cost to fence it if one meter of fencing costs $9?

35 m

50 m

3. Henry ran around a rectangular field of length 175 m and width 80 m three times. Find the total distance that he ran.

4. A rectangular piece of cardboard is 3 times as long as it is wide. If it is 25 cm wide, find its perimeter.

5. What is the perimeter of this figure?

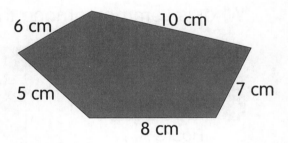

6. A wire is used to form a rectangle of length 12 cm and width 9 cm. What is the length of the wire?

7. A wire of length 75 cm was used to form a square. If 3 cm of it was not used, find the length of the square.

8. Each square in the following figures has an area of 1 square unit. Find the area and perimeter of each figure. What is common among these figures?

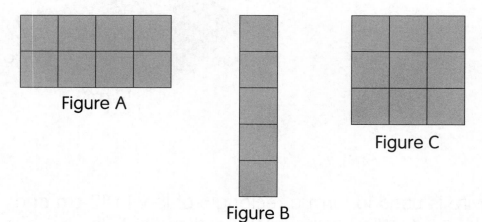

Figure A

Figure B

Figure C

Worked Example 1

Square ABCD is formed by 9 small squares. The perimeter of each small square is 8 cm. Find the perimeter of square ABCD.

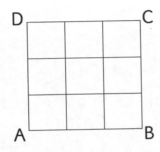

Length of each small square = 8 cm ÷ 4 = 2 cm

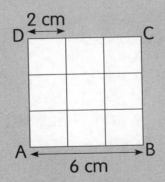

Length of square ABCD = 2 cm × 3 = 6 cm

Perimeter of square ABCD = 6 cm × 4 = 24 cm

The perimeter of square ABCD is **24 cm**.

Worked Example 2

What is the perimeter of the figure below?

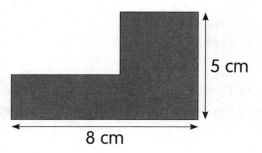

5 cm

8 cm

Shift the lines as shown by the arrows.
They form a rectangle of length 8 cm and width
5 cm.

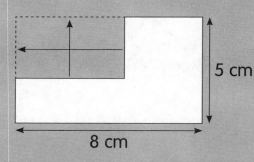

5 cm

8 cm

The given figure and
the rectangle have
the same perimeter.

Perimeter = length + width + length + width
           = 8 cm + 5 cm + 8 cm + 5 cm
           = 26 cm

The perimeter of the figure is **26 cm**.

Worked Example 3

The square is made up of 3 identical rectangles. The perimeter of the square is 36 cm. What is the perimeter of each rectangle?

Perimeter of square = 36 cm
Length of square = 36 cm ÷ 4 = 9 cm
Length of rectangle = 9 cm
Width of rectangle = 9 cm ÷ 3 = 3 cm

Perimeter of rectangle
= length + width + length + width
= 9 cm + 3 cm + 9 cm + 3 cm
= 24 cm

The perimeter of each rectangle is **24 cm**.

Answer all questions. Show your work and write your statements clearly.

1. Find the perimeter of each of the following figures.

    (a)

    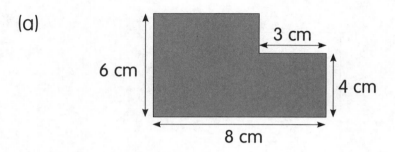

    (b)

    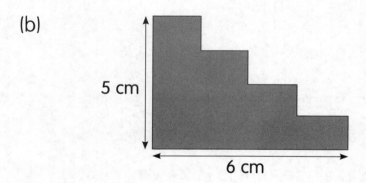

2. Find the perimeter of each of the following hexagons (six-sided figures).

(a)

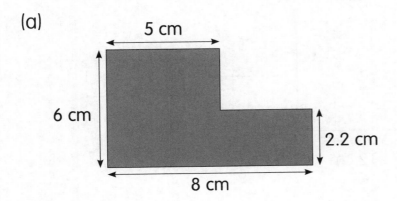

5 cm

6 cm

2.2 cm

8 cm

(b)

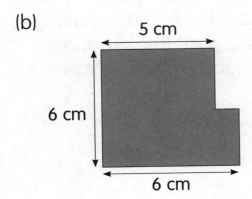

5 cm

6 cm

6 cm

3. A square of side 12 cm has four of its corners cut off. What is the perimeter of the new figure?

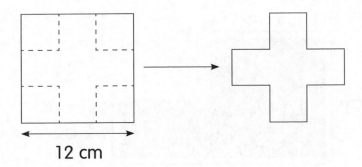

12 cm

4. Farmer Oates has an orchard 24 m long and 24 m wide. His orange trees are planted 8 m apart along the perimeter of the orchard. If each tree produces 100 oranges, how many oranges will he get from his orchard?

5. The figure consists of 5 squares, each of side 6 cm. What is the perimeter of the figure?

6. The square is made up of 3 identical rectangles. The perimeter of each rectangle is 16 cm. What is the perimeter of the square?

7. Find the area of each figure drawn on the square grid.

(a)

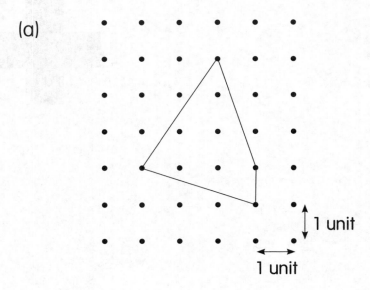

1 unit

1 unit

(b)

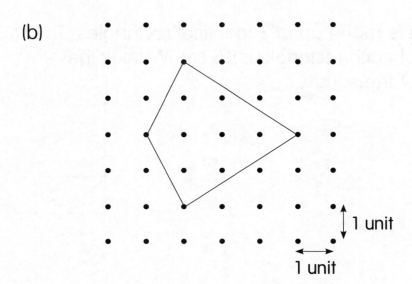

1 unit

1 unit

13 Mixed Problems 1

Worked Example 1

A container has a capacity of 3 liters. 1 *l* 50 ml of water is poured into it. How much more water must be added to fill the container completely?

3 *l* – 1 *l* 50 ml = 1 *l* 950 ml

3 *l*

2 *l*   1 *l* – 50 ml = 950 ml

1 *l* 950 ml of water must be added to fill the container.

Worked Example 2

Sally began her lesson at 4:05 p.m. However, the lesson took 30 minutes longer than usual and ended at 6:25 p.m. How long did the lesson usually last?

4:05 p.m. $\xrightarrow{\text{2 h}}$ 6:05 p.m. $\xrightarrow{\text{20 min}}$ 6:25 p.m.

From 4:05 p.m. to 6:25 p.m., there are 2 h 20 min.

2 h 20 min − 30 min = $\underbrace{\text{2 h 20 min − 20 min}}_{\text{2 h}}$ − 10 min

= 1 h 50 min

The lesson usually lasted **1 h 50 min**.

Answer all questions. Show your work and write your statements clearly.

1. A full large jug can fill 2 small jugs. A full small jug can fill 5 cups. How many cups can be filled with a full large jug?

2. A jewelry shop opens at 10:00 a.m. every day and closes at 9:30 p.m. How long is the shop open each day?

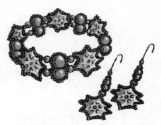

3. (a) What is the largest three-digit number?
   (b) What is the smallest four-digit number?

4. Yvonne rented 5 DVDs from her club. The rental charge for each DVD was the same. If she paid $2.50 for postage and her total bill was $17.50, find the rental charge for one DVD.

5. Write down the next three terms in the number sequence below.

   8, 13, 11, 16, 14, _____, _____, _____

6. I am thinking of a three-digit odd number. The three digits add up to 10. The tens digit is twice the hundreds digit. There are no zeros. What number am I thinking of?

7. A wire measuring 72 cm long is cut equally into three pieces. The shorter pieces of wire are bent to make three identical triangles of equal sides. What is the length of one side of a triangle?

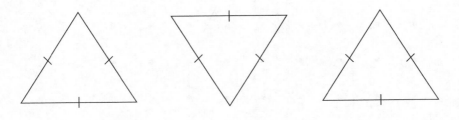

8. Given that $\square$ + $\triangle$ = 110

and $\square$ + $\triangle$ + $\triangle$ = 200,

find the value of $\square$ and of $\triangle$.

9. What is the area of the figure drawn on the square grid?

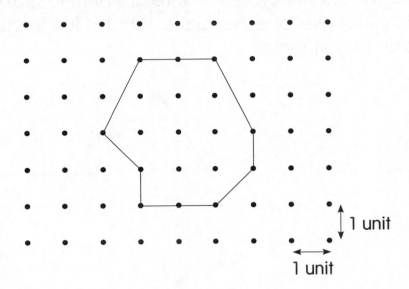

1 unit

1 unit

10. Susan spent $\frac{1}{3}$ of her pocket money on food and $\frac{1}{2}$ of what was left on a drink. If she had $10 left, how much was her pocket money?

11. If the square and the triangle below have the same perimeter, what is the length of the square?

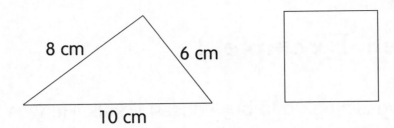

8 cm   6 cm

10 cm

12. A pen, a pencil and two erasers cost $4.00. An eraser and a pen cost $2.70, and a pencil costs $0.80. What is the cost of an eraser?

Challenging Problems

Worked Example 1

Tommy was lining up to buy concert tickets. He was 29th in the line. From the end of the line, he was in the 34th position. How many people were there in the line?

Since Tommy was 29th from the front, there were 28 people in front of him. Since he was 34th from the end, there were 33 people behind him.

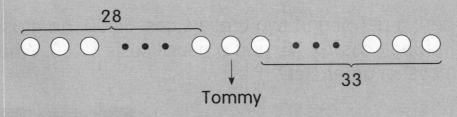

$28 + 1 + 33 = 62$

There were **62** people in the line.

Worked Example 2

The figure below is made up of 6 squares. Divide the figure into 4 identical shapes.

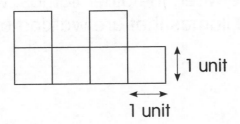

1 unit

1 unit

The figure is made up of 6 squares.
The area of the figure is 6 square units.

$\frac{1}{4}$ of 4 = 1

$\frac{1}{4}$ of 2 = $\frac{1}{2}$

The area of each shape will be $1\frac{1}{2}$ square units.

One possible division is as follows:

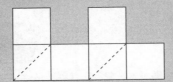

Answer all questions. Show your work and write your statements clearly.

1. Some llamas are walking over the hill. One llama is in front of three llamas. One llama is behind three llamas. Two llamas are between the other llamas. What is the fewest number of llamas that are walking over the hill?

2. How many times does the digit '1' appear in numbers from 1 to 100?

3. Veronica spent $9.90 on a book. She spent $6.35 more on a teddy bear than the book. If she had $2.20 left, how much money did she have at first?

4. Joel was in a line at an amusement park to take a ride. He was the 36th person from the front and 43rd person from the end of the line. How many people were in the line?

5. John had a bagel as shown below. He shared his bagel with four friends. He used only 2 straight cuts to divide the bagel into five pieces. If each piece was not of the same size, how did he divide the bagel into 5 pieces?

6. Alfred is 6 years older than his sister. Five years ago, he was 11 years old. How old is his sister now?

7. Irene bought 15 packets of snacks, each weighing 3 oz.
    Theresa bought 9 packets of snacks, each weighing 5 oz.
    (a) How many ounces of snacks did they buy in total?
    (b) One of the girls dropped some packets of snacks
        while they were walking home. They found that they
        had 20 oz less snacks.
        (i) Who dropped her snacks?
        (ii) How many packets were dropped?

8. Rose made a necklace with different colored beads. She
    followed a pattern: 2 red beads, 1 blue bead, then
    1 green bead. The pattern is repeated and she used a
    total of 5 green beads to make the necklace. How many
    beads did she use altogether?

9. One kilogram of grade A flour costs $6.50. One kilogram of grade B flour costs $4.00. Two kilograms of grade A flour are mixed with three kilograms of grade B flour to produce grade C flour. How much does one kilogram of grade C flour cost?

10. There were 13 cars and bicycles in a car park. If there were 44 wheels altogether, how many cars were in the car park?

11. The figure below is made up of 4 identical squares. Divide the figure into 4 equal parts using only two cuts.

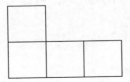

14 Mixed Problems 2

Worked Example 1

In the figure below, the perimeter of the rectangle is twice that of the square. What is the perimeter of the rectangle?

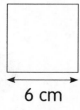

6 cm

Perimeter of square = 6 cm × 4
= 24 cm

Perimeter of rectangle = 24 cm × 2
= 48 cm

The perimeter of the rectangle is **48 cm**.

Worked Example 2

How many digits are used to print the page numbers in *Math Can Be Fun* which has 200 pages?

Page Numbers	Number of Digits
1 – 9	9
10 – 99	$99 - 10 + 1 = 90$ $90 \times 2 = 180$
100 – 200	$200 - 100 + 1 = 101$ $101 \times 3 = 303$

$9 + 180 + 303 = 492$

492 digits are used to print the page numbers in *Math Can Be Fun.*

Practice Questions

Answer all questions. Show your work clearly.

1. Write down the next two terms in each sequence.

   (a) 1, 1, 2, 3, 5, 8, 13, _____, _____

   (b) 1, 4, 9, 16, _____, _____

2. What fraction of each figure is shaded?
   (a)   (b)   (c)

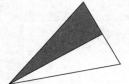 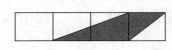

3. Joseph left school and took 1 h 35 min to reach home. If he reached home at 5:30 p.m., at what time did he leave his school?

4. Eddy's score in a mathematics test is in the 14th position from both the highest and the lowest scores. How many students took the test?

5. The total weight of a mango and a guava is 1350 g. The guava is 580 g heavier than the mango. What is the weight of the mango?

6. Ian had three large identical boxes to contain three different types of balls as shown below. If each box is completely filled with only one type of ball, find the box with the
   (a) least number of balls,
   (b) the most number of balls.

7. Five friends met at a concert. Each person shook hands with the other four. How many handshakes took place?

8. A farmer picked 1200 apples from his orchard. He gave away 240 of them to his relatives and packed the rest into bags of 8 each.
   (a) How many bags of apples were there altogether?
   (b) If he sold each bag of apples for $3, how much money did he collect?

9. The area of two parts of a circle is given below. What is the area of the shaded part?

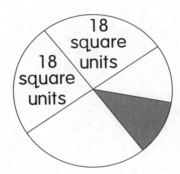

10. Five children are in a line to see the dentist. Dennis is the next one in line. Cathy is standing behind Aaron. Aaron is two places in front of Betty. Esther is in line next to Aaron. List the order of the five children in the line starting with the first one.

11. Sam has 64 marbles. Ray has 36 marbles. How many marbles must Sam give to Ray so that each has the same number of marbles? How many marbles will each have?

12. Pail X has a capacity of 9 liters. Pail Y has a capacity of 2 liters. How can you use pails X and Y to measure out 3 liters of water?

13. Dave has 97 stickers. Mark has twice as many stickers as Dave. Roy has three times as many stickers as Mark. How many stickers does Roy have?

Challenging Problems

Worked Example

Jenny walked from her house to school and then to the library. After borrowing some books from the library, she walked home using the same route. What was the total distance she travelled? Express your answer in kilometers and meters.

Jenny's house

1 km 250 m

970 m

House	1 km 250 m	School	970 m	Library
	1 km 250 m		970 m	

1 km 250 m + 1 km 250 m + 970 m + 970 m
= 4 km 440 m

Jenny travelled a total distance of **4 km 440 m**.

Answer all questions. Show your work and write your statements clearly.

1. At a stadium, there were 4054 children and 128 teachers. The number of parents was 3656 fewer than the total number of children and teachers. How many parents were there?

2. A six-sided die rests on a table. When Rose walks around the table, she counts and adds the dots on all the faces of the die that she can see. There is a total of 16 dots. What is the number of dots on the face resting on the table?

3. In the following addition, the letters A, B and C stand for different digits. Which digit does each letter represent?

$$
\begin{array}{r}
B\ A \\
+\ B\ A \\
\hline
C\ A\ A \\
\end{array}
$$

4. How many three-digit numbers are there, such that the ones digit and hundreds digit are the same, but the tens digit is three more than the ones digit?

5. Signal lights are located 25 m apart along an underground tunnel. There is a total of 8 signal lights in the tunnel. If there are signal lights at the beginning and end of the tunnel, how long is the tunnel?

6. Use the digits 0, 2, 4, 5, 6 and 7 to fill the following boxes to obtain the greatest possible difference.

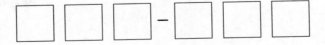

7. Cynthia had $16.75. She withdrew more cash from an ATM before shopping. After spending $17.50 on a box of cookies and $23.40 on a box of chocolates, she had $35.85 left. How much money did she withdraw from the ATM?

8. Mr. Smith bought a new television for $304 and saved $9 on his electricity bill each month as compared to using an old television. How many months of savings on his electricity bill will allow him to get a second television of the same price?

9. What is the largest two-digit number that can be divided by 2 and 3 without any remainder?

10. A rectangle with an area of 36 square units is shown below.

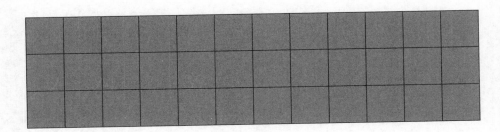

How many ways can you arrange 36 such square units to form a rectangle?

11. The figure below is made up of squares. If the perimeter of each square is 12 cm, find the perimeter of the figure.

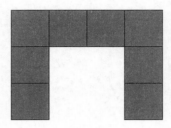

12. Study the sequence below.

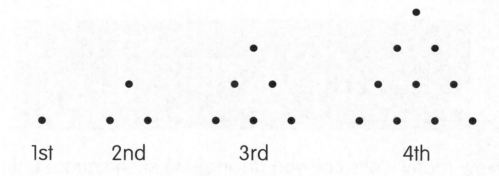

1st   2nd   3rd   4th

(a) Draw the 5th figure.
(b) How many dots are there in the 10th figure?

15 Mixed Problems 3

Worked Example 1

A total of 852 digits are used to print the page numbers of a book. How many pages does the book have?

Page Numbers	Number of digits
1 – 9	9
10 – 99	99 – 10 + 1 = 90 90 × 2 = 180

852 – 9 – 180 = 663

663 digits are used for 3-digit page numbers.

663 ÷ 3 = 221

There are 221 3-digit pages.

221 + 9 + 90 = 320

The book has **320** pages.

Worked Example 2

How many digits are there in all the numbers from 1 to 500?

Numbers	Number of digits
1 – 9	9
10 – 99	99 – 10 + 1 = 90 90 × 2 = 180
100 – 500	500 – 100 + 1 = 401 401 × 3 = 1203

9 + 180 + 1203 = 1392

There are **1392** digits.

Practice Questions

Answer all questions. Show your work and write your statements clearly.

1. There were 18 people in a line at a ticket counter. 10 people were in line behind John. How many people were in line in front of him?

2. A snail falls into a well that is 10 meters deep. During the day, it can crawl up 3 meters. At night, it slips down by 1 meter. How many days will it take the snail to get out of the well?

3. Tracy plans to buy a plasma TV that costs $1395. When she counts her savings, she realizes that she is short of $165. How much money does she have?

4. A movie lasts 1 h 18 min. At what time must the movie start so that it will end by midnight?

5. Elizabeth has 300 more buttons than Paul at first. She gives 150 buttons to him. Who has more buttons now?

6. I am thinking of a number that is less than 1000 but greater than 459. The hundreds digit is even and is 2 less than the ones digit. The tens digit is half the ones digit. What number am I thinking of?

7. The diagram below shows the scores on a dart board.

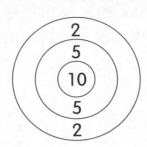

Arthur scored 21 points. What is the least number of darts needed to achieve that score?

8. Look at the figures below.
   Then fill in the missing numbers in the boxes.

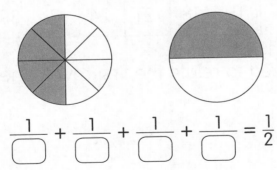

$$\frac{1}{\boxed{}} + \frac{1}{\boxed{}} + \frac{1}{\boxed{}} + \frac{1}{\boxed{}} = \frac{1}{2}$$

9. Three brothers, Tim, Tom and Ted, went on a vacation together. Tim spent $2180, which is $390 more than what Tom spent. Ted spent $265 less than Tom. How much did Ted spend?

10. Study the pattern and complete the table.

2	3	4	5	7	?
15	18	21	24	?	39

(Hint: You need to relate the first row to the second row.)

Worked Example

A survey was conducted among a group of students on their favorite type of movie.
Study the bar graph and answer the following questions.

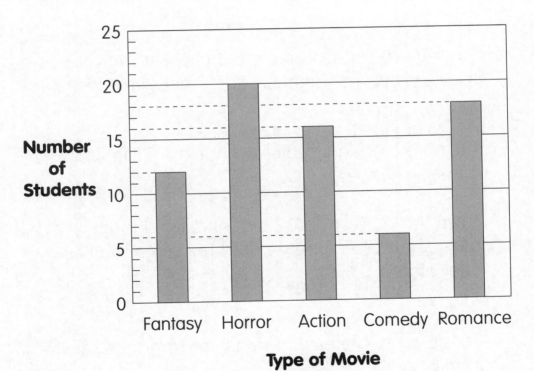

Type of Movie

(a) How many more students preferred horror movies to comedy movies?

(b) How many students preferred fantasy or romance movies in all?

(c) The number of students who liked romance movies is three times the number of students who liked comedy movies.
Is the statement true or false? Explain your answer.

(d) How many students took part in the survey?

(e) The total number of students who liked horror and action movies was more than the total number of students who liked fantasy, romance and comedy movies.
Is the statement true or false? Explain your answer.

(a) From the bar graph, 20 students liked horror movies and 6 students liked comedy movies.

$$20 - 6 = 14$$

14 more students preferred horror movies to comedy movies.

(b) From the bar graph, 12 students liked fantasy movies and 18 students liked romance movies altogether.

$$12 + 18 = 30$$

30 students preferred fantasy or romance movies in all.

(c) The statement is **true**.

From the bar graph, 18 students liked romance movies and 6 liked comedy movies.

18 ÷ 6 = 3

Therefore, the number of students who liked romance movies is three times the number of students who liked comedy movies.

(d)

Type of movies	Number of students
Fantasy	12
Horror	20
Action	16
Comedy	6
Romance	18
Total	72

12 + 20 + 16 + 6 + 18 = 72

72 students took part in the survey.

(e) The total number of students who liked horror and action movies is 20 + 16 = 36.

The total number of students who liked fantasy, romance and comedy movies is 12 + 18 + 6 = 36.

The statement is **false**.

The total number of students who liked horror and action movies was the same as the total number of students who liked fantasy, romance and comedy movies.

Answer all questions. Show your work and write your statements clearly.

1. Jenny has $100 in her money box now. If she saves $10 every month, how much will she have in her money box after one year?

2. Arthur bought some pears. He gave the fruit seller a $50 bill and received $38 change. If 3 pears cost $1, how many pears did he buy altogether?

3. Using the numbers 1 to 9 only once, place them in the circles so that the sum of the numbers in each line is 15.

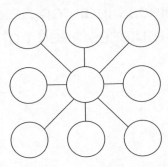

(Hint: Look for sets of three numbers that add up to 15.)

4. Hamid delivered some snakes and spiders to a zoo. The zookeeper counted 48 legs and 22 heads. How many snakes and how many spiders were there?

5. A straight cut will slice a circle into 2 pieces; two cuts will slice a circle into a maximum of 4 pieces. What is the most number of pieces that can be obtained from 5 straight cuts? The pieces need not be of the same sizes.

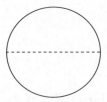

1 cut, 2 pieces

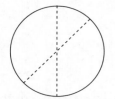

2 cuts, 4 pieces

6. Study the diagrams below.
    Then fill in the missing numbers in the boxes.

    (a)

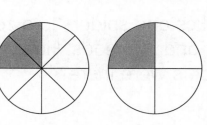

$$\frac{1}{8} = \frac{1}{4} - \frac{1}{\boxed{}}$$

    (b)

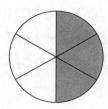

$$\frac{1}{6} + \frac{1}{6} = \frac{1}{2} - \frac{1}{\boxed{}}$$

7. Four students, Ann, Jean, Karen and Sue, borrowed books from a library. Each person was allowed to borrow a maximum of six books. They borrowed a total of 15 books. Karen borrowed two books and Jean borrowed three books. How many books did Ann borrow if Sue borrowed the most number of books?

8. Lisa bought 11 pens and erasers for $5.00. A pen cost 50¢ and an eraser cost 40¢.
   (a) How many erasers did she buy?
   (b) What is the total cost of the pens?

9. The figure below shows a square formed by 4 identical rectangles. The perimeter of each rectangle is 50 cm. What is the length of the square?

10. During a marathon, 46 cups of water were consumed by 13 children. If each girl drank 3 cups of water and each boy drank 4 cups of water, how many boys and how many girls were there?

11. Albert cut a wire into two pieces to make the following rectangles.

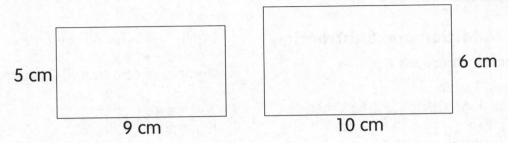

5 cm

9 cm

6 cm

10 cm

What is the length of the original wire?

12. How many right angles are there in the figure below?

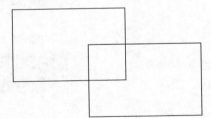

Answers

1 Addition and Subtraction

Practice Questions (pp. 4-7)

1. 4821 stamps
2. (a) 1554 men   (b) 658 men
3. $1495
4. 21 pages
5. (a) 2433 stickers (b) 2641 stickers
6. 85 stamps
7. 390 fruits
8. 11 times (10, 20, 30, 40, 50, 60, 70, 80, 90, 100)
9. 2018 people
10. Richard; 100 marbles

Challenging Problems (pp. 9-13)

1. (a) P = 1023   (b) Q = 549
   (c) P + Q = 1572
2. 9 years old
3. 10 toy cars
4. 20 times (9, 19, 29, …, 89, 90, 91, …, 99)
5. Q + S = 9
   P + R = 15
   P + Q + R + S = 9 + 15
               = 24
6. If all animals have 2 legs, there will be 15 × 2 = 30 legs.
   44 − 30 = 14
   Flamingoes have 2 legs and wild cats have 4 legs. Wild cats have 2 more legs than flamingoes.
   Number of wild cats = 14 ÷ 2 = 7
7.

   Nickels [ ]·····| } ?
   17 43
   Dimes [ ]

1 unit ⟶ 17 + 43 = 60
3 units ⟶ 3 × 60 = 180
Number of coins left = 180 coins

8. 259 loaves
9. 19 numbers (6, 16, 26, …, 60, 61, …, 69, 76, 86, 96)
10.

← 1st tear

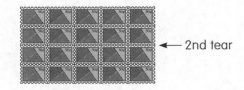
← 2nd tear

← 3rd tear

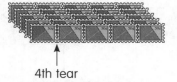
4th tear

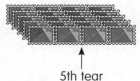
5th tear

6th tear

Least number of times = 6

2 Multiplication and Division

Practice Questions (pp. 17-21)

1. 83 coins
2. 15 pens
3. 39 apples
4. Total number of coins = 126×7
   $\qquad = 882$
   Number of coins in each bigger
   bag = $882 \div 3 = 294$
5. 201 postcards
6. 192 stickers
7. 168 stamps
8. 94 paper cranes
9. 13 tricycles
10. (a) $210
    (b) Teddy: $1050; Sally: $1010
11. Least number of candies in the
    bag = $3 \times 4 \times 5 = 60$
12. Cost of 3 clocks = $42 \times 3 = $126
    Cost of 1 watch = $126 + $35
    $\qquad = $161
    Cost of 6 watches = $161 \times 6
    $\qquad = $966

Challenging Problems (pp. 24-28)

1. 30 blue balloons and 55 green
   balloons
2. 476 postcards
3. Total length of 8 cars = 8×16 m
   $\qquad = 128$ m
   Total distance between the cars
   = 142 m – 128 m
   = 14 m
   Distance between neighboring
   cars = 14 m $\div$ 7
   $\qquad = 2$ m
4. 3 buses, 24 seats
5. 19 students
6.

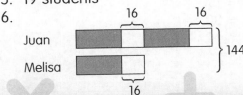

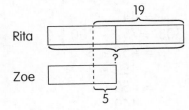

$3 \,\boxed{} \longrightarrow 144 - 16 - 16 - 16$
$\qquad\qquad = 96$
$1 \,\boxed{} \longrightarrow 96 \div 3$
$\qquad\qquad = 32$
Number of coins Juan had at first
= 32 + 16 + 32 + 16 + 16
= 112

7. 24 – 5 = 19

1 unit $\longrightarrow$ 19 – 5 = 14
2 units $\longrightarrow$ $2 \times 14 = 28$
Number of barrettes Rita had left
= 28

8. Jason: 10 cans, Louis: 15 cans
9. 5 red envelopes and 6 blue
   envelopes
10. 4 rock bears

3 Mental Calculation

Practice Questions (pp. 33-34)

1. 56 + 9 = 56 + 10 – 1
   $\qquad = 66 – 1$
   $\qquad = 65$
2. 728 + 98 = 726 + 2 + 98
   $\qquad = 726 + 100$
   $\qquad = 826$
3. 145 – 99 = 146 – 1 – 99
   $\qquad = 146 – 100$
   $\qquad = 46$
4. 706 – 198 = 706 – 200 + 2
   $\qquad = 506 + 2$
   $\qquad = 508$
5. $25 \times 6 = 20 \times 6 + 5 \times 6$
   $\qquad = 120 + 30$
   $\qquad = 150$

or

$25 \times 6 = 25 \times 4 + 25 \times 2$
$\qquad = 100 + 50$
$\qquad = 150$

6. $35 \times 8 = 30 \times 8 + 5 \times 8$
$\qquad = 240 + 40$
$\qquad = 280$

7. $198 + 243 = 198 + 2 + 241$
$\qquad = 200 + 241$
$\qquad = 441$

8. $752 - 303 = 752 - 300 - 3$
$\qquad = 452 - 3$
$\qquad = 452 - 2 - 1$
$\qquad = 450 - 1$
$\qquad = 449$

9. $505 \times 9 = 500 \times 9 + 5 \times 9$
$\qquad = 4500 + 45$
$\qquad = 4545$

10. $82 \times 6 = 80 \times 6 + 2 \times 6$
$\qquad = 480 + 12$
$\qquad = 492$

11. $57 \times 3 = 50 \times 3 + 7 \times 3$
$\qquad = 150 + 21$
$\qquad = 171$

12. $209 \times 7 = 200 \times 7 + 9 \times 7$
$\qquad = 1400 + 63$
$\qquad = 1463$

13. $49 \times 5 = 40 \times 5 + 9 \times 5$
$\qquad = 200 + 45$
$\qquad = 245$

14. $809 \times 3 = 800 \times 3 + 9 \times 3$
$\qquad = 2400 + 27$
$\qquad = 2427$

Challenging Problems (pp. 38-39)

1. $158 + 93 + 42 = 158 + 42 + 93$
$\qquad = 200 + 93$
$\qquad = 293$

2. $997 + 605 = 997 + 3 + 602$
$\qquad = 1000 + 602$
$\qquad = 1602$

3. $74 + 37 + 49$
$\qquad = 70 + 1 + 3 + 37 + 49$
$\qquad = 70 + 40 + 50$
$\qquad = 160$

4. $234 + 567$
$\qquad = 200 + 34 + 500 + 66 + 1$
$\qquad = 700 + 100 + 1$
$\qquad = 801$

5. $7000 - 137 = 6999 - 137 + 1$
$\qquad = 6862 + 1$
$\qquad = 6863$

6. $10{,}000 - 894 = 9999 - 894 + 1$
$\qquad = 9105 + 1$
$\qquad = 9106$

7. $126 - 75 = 26 + 25$
$\qquad = 51$

8. $163 - 92 = 63 + 8$
$\qquad = 71$

9. 116
10. 1500
11. 46
12. 370
13. 425
14. 2310
15. 124
16. 181

4   Bar Graphs

Practice Questions (pp. 46–51)

1. (a) Science   (b) 2 students
   (c) Total number of students
   $\qquad = 8 + 12 + 10 + 13$
   $\qquad = 43$

2. Number of students who like red, blue and purple
   $= 50 + 70 + 30$
   $= 150$
   Number of students who like purple
   $= 150 \div 5$
   $= 30$

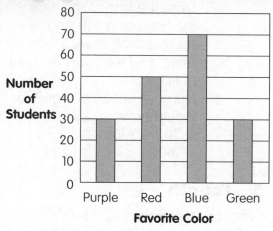

Favorite Color

3. (a) 35 students (b) Blue
   (c) 10 students
4. (a) Tennis (b) 55 students
   (c) 110 students
5. (a) 33 adults
   (b) train; bicycle
   (c) 7 adults
   (d) 9
6. (a) Internet Games
   (b) 500 teenagers
   (c) 450 teenagers
   (d) 500 teenagers
   (e) 550 teenagers

Challenging Problems (pp. 57-62)

1. (a) Number of souvenirs
      distributed from Tuesday to
      Thursday
      = 40 + 35 + 55
      = 130
   (b) Number of souvenirs prepared
      = 130 + 20 + 50 + 15
      = 215
2. (a) From the bar graph, the
      longest bar is the one
      representing Ian.
      Ian took the longest time. He
      was the slowest swimmer.
   (b) From the bar graph, the
      shortest bar is the one
      representing Claire.

Claire took the shortest time.
She was the fastest swimmer.
   (c) From the bar graph, the
      second longest bar is the one
      representing Paul.
      Paul was the second last
      swimmer.
   (d) From the bar graph, the
      third shortest bar is the one
      representing Bob.
      Bob came in third.
3. (a) 3
   (b) 25
   (c) 2006; 2008
4. (a)

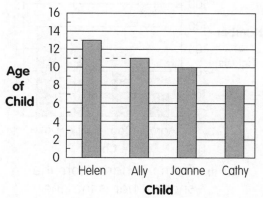

Country

   (b) (i) Malaysia (ii) Brunei
      (iii) 35 (iv) 115
5. (a)

Child

   (b) (i) Total age of Helen and Cathy
      = 13 years old + 8 years old
      = 21 years old

(ii) Number of years for Joanne
to reach Helen's age
= 13 − 10
= 3
Age of Ally
= 11 years old + 3 years old
= 14 years old

(iii) Number of years for Cathy
to reach Joanne's age
= 10 − 8
= 2
Age of Helen
= 13 years old + 2 years old
= 15 years old

6. (a)

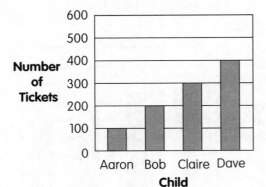

10 □ → 1000
1 □ → 100
2 □ → 200
4 □ → 400
3 □ → 300

Number of Tickets

600
500
400
300
200
100
0

Aaron Bob Claire Dave

Child

(b) (i) From the bar graph, the
shortest bar is the one
representing Aaron.
Aaron sold the least
number of tickets.

(ii) From the bar graph, the
longest bar is the one
representing Dave.
Dave sold the most number
of tickets.

(iii) Number of tickets that Bob
would have to sell
= 300 − 200
= 100

5   Length

Practice Questions (pp. 66-69)

1.

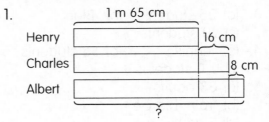

Height of Albert
= 1 m 65 cm + 16 cm + 8 cm
= 1 m 89 cm

2. 35 cm

3.

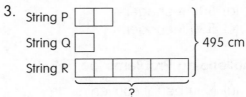

9 units → 495 cm
1 unit → 495 cm ÷ 9
= 55 cm
6 units → 6 × 55 cm
= 330 cm
Length of string R
= 330 cm or 3 m 30 cm

4. 2 m 8 cm
5. 1 m 30 cm
6. Kelly: 4 ft 10 in.; Adeline is taller by
6 in.
7. 5 m 80 cm

8.

9 – 1 = 8 intervals

120 cm 120 cm   120 cm 120 cm
○←→○←→○ ・・・ ○←→○←→○

120 cm × 8 = 960 cm

960 cm = 9 m 60 cm

9. 6 m 9 cm

10. 840 yd

Challenging Problems (pp. 72-75)

1. Before

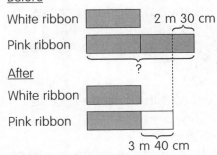

White ribbon   2 m 30 cm

Pink ribbon

After   ?

White ribbon

Pink ribbon

3 m 40 cm

1 ▢ ⟶ 3 m 40 cm + 2 m
        30 cm
        = 5 m 70 cm

2 ▢ ⟶ 5 m 70 cm + 5 m
        70 cm
        = 11 m 40 cm

Length of pink ribbon = 11 m 40 cm

2. 3 km 500 m

3. Before   120 ft

Ribbon X

Ribbon Y

After

Ribbon X

Ribbon Y

1 unit ⟶ 120 ft
4 units ⟶ 4 × 120 ft
          = 480 ft

Total length of ribbons X and Y at
first = 480 ft
     = 160 yd

4. 5 ft 1 in.

5.

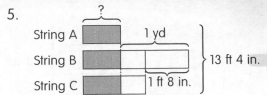

String A   1 yd

String B   } 13 ft 4 in.

String C   1 ft 8 in.

3 ft – 1 ft 8 in. = 1 ft 4 in.

3 ▢ ⟶ 13 ft 4 in. – 3 ft – 1 ft 4 in.
        = 9 ft

1 ▢ ⟶ 9 ft ÷ 3
        = 3 ft

Length of string A = 3 ft or 1 yd

6. Before   5 m 70 cm

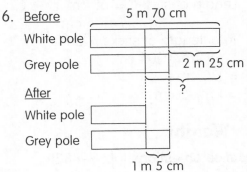

White pole

Grey pole   2 m 25 cm

After   ?

White pole

Grey pole

1 m 5 cm

Length of the white pole that was
cut off = 2 m 25 cm + 1 m 5 cm
            = 3 m 30 cm

7. 67 yd

8. 1 m 60 cm

9.

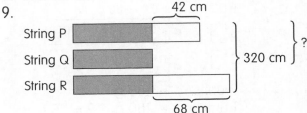

String P   42 cm

String Q   } 320 cm   } ?

String R

68 cm

3 ▢ ⟶ 320 cm – 42 cm – 68 cm
        = 210 cm

1 ▢ ⟶ 210 cm ÷ 3
        = 70 cm

Length of string Q = 70 cm
Length of string P = 70 cm + 42 cm
            = 112 cm

Total length of strings P and Q
= 112 cm + 70 cm
= 182 cm
= 1 m 82 cm

10.

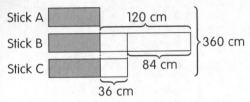

$3\ \blacksquare \longrightarrow 360\ cm - 120\ cm - 36\ cm$
$\qquad = 204\ cm$

$1\ \blacksquare \longrightarrow 204\ cm \div 3$
$\qquad = 68\ cm$

Length of stick A = 68 cm
Length of stick C = 68 cm + 36 cm
$\qquad\qquad\qquad = 104\ cm$

Total length of sticks A and C
= 68 cm + 104 cm
= 172 cm
= 1 m 72 cm

6 Weight

Practice Questions (pp. 79–82)

1. 415 g
2. 3 oz
3. 42 lb
4. 142 lb
5. 740 g
6.

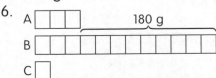

9 units $\longrightarrow$ 180 g
1 unit $\longrightarrow$ 180 g ÷ 9 = 20 g
10 units $\longrightarrow$ 10 × 20 g = 200 g
11 units $\longrightarrow$ 20 g + 200 g
$\qquad\qquad\qquad = 220\ g$

Bag C is 220 g lighter than bag B.

7. 17 kg
8. 132 g
9. 22 lb 1 oz
10. (a) 2 kg 250 g   (b) 8 kg 275 g
11. 162 lb
12. 600 g

Challenging Problems (pp. 86–90)

1. 1 kg 100 g
2. 100 g
3. (a) 1 kg 625 g   (b) 3 kg 480 g
   (c) 1 kg 405 g
4. 220 lb
5. 540 g
6. (a) 1 kg 190 g   (b) 755 g
   (c) 745 g
7. (a) 28 kg   (b) 17 kg
8. One triangle and two circles
9. (a) 90 g   (b) 400 g
10. Cost of 2 lb of grade A coffee
    = $11 × 2
    = $22
    Cost of 3 lb of grade C coffee
    = $6 × 3
    = $18
    2 lb of grade A coffee + 3 lb of
    grade C coffee = 5 lb of grade B
    coffee
    Cost of 5 lb of grade B coffee
    = $22 + $18
    = $40
    Cost of 1 lb of grade B coffee
    = $40 ÷ 5
    = $8

7 Capacity

Practice Questions (pp. 94–98)

1. 3 l 160 ml
2. Amount of water when the tank is
   half filled = 83 gal – 29 gal
   $\qquad\qquad = 54\ gal$
   Capacity of the tank
   = 54 gal × 2 = 108 gal
3. 1 l 980 ml
4. 2 gal 1 qt
5. 9 l 110 ml
6. 5 l 500 ml
7. 2 qt
8. 2 l 290 ml

9. Capacity of pot Q = 725 ml × 6
$\qquad\qquad\qquad\quad$ = 4350 ml
$\quad$ Capacity of pot R
$\quad$ = 4350 ml − 2590 ml
$\quad$ = 1760 ml
$\quad$ = 1 l 760 ml
10. Volume of water in bucket B
$\quad$ = 440 ml × 2
$\quad$ = 880 ml
$\quad$ Volume of water in bucket C
$\quad$ = 440 ml ÷ 2
$\quad$ = 220 ml
$\quad$ Volume of water in buckets B and C
$\quad$ = 880 ml + 220 ml
$\quad$ = 1100 ml
$\quad$ = 1 l 110 ml

Challenging Problems (pp. 102–105)

1. (a) 260 ml $\qquad$ (b) 330 ml
2. (a)

3 l	7 l
0	7
3	4
0	4
3	1

(b)

3 l	7 l
0	7
3	4
0	4
3	1
0	1
1	0
1	7
3	5

3. (a) David: 6; Ruth: 5
$\quad$ (b) 1 l 200 ml
4. Amount of liquid X required to
$\quad$ make 2 l of soup
$\quad$ = 2 l ÷ 2
$\quad$ = 1 l = 1000 ml
$\quad$ Number of cans required
$\quad$ = 1000 ml ÷ 100 ml
$\quad$ = 10
5. 36 gal
6. 10 l
7.

3 l	5 l	8 l
0	5	0
3	0	2
0	5	2
3	0	4

8.

2 ▢ ⟶ 10 l − 9 l = 1 l
$\qquad\qquad\qquad\quad$ = 1000 ml
1 ▢ ⟶ 1000 ÷ 2 = 500 ml
Capacity of the jug = 500 ml
9. 880 ml
10.

5 l	9 l	Container
5	0	7
0	5	7
5	5	2
1	9	2
1	0	11
0	1	11
5	1	6
0	6	6

8 Money

Practice Questions (pp. 109-113)

1. $104.20
2. $34.60
3. $8.40
4. $23.50
5. $3.75
6. $2.35
7. $25
8. 12 weeks
9. Roy: $54, June: $83
10. (a) 2 × 10¢ + 22¢
$\qquad$ Two 10¢ stamps and one 22¢
$\qquad$ stamp were used to mail
$\qquad$ package 1.
$\quad$ (b) 10¢ + 3 × 22¢
$\qquad$ One 10¢ stamp and three 22¢
$\qquad$ stamps were used to mail
$\qquad$ package 2.

(c) 2 × 22¢ + 50¢
Two 22¢ stamps and one 50¢ stamp were used to mail package 3.
11. $13
12. Number of pairs of erasers
= 10 ÷ 2
= 5
Amount that Andrew paid
= 5 × 90¢ = 450¢
= $4.50

Challenging Problems (pp. 116-120)

1. 12 fish
2. $36.45
3. Mr. Yang, cheaper by 20¢
4. $300
5. Assume the worst case:
The first 3 balls obtained are of different colors.
The 4th ball will match any of the three colors.
The least amount of money that I need to spend is $4.
6. $140
7. Adam: $24.10; Pam: $34
8. $15.30 = 1530¢
1530¢ ÷ 9 = 170¢
$2 = 200¢
200¢ − 170¢ = 30¢
9. 1568 quarters
10. $1.30
11. Shorts and Jacket
12.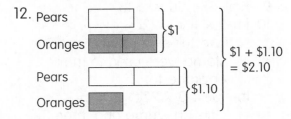

3 pears and 3 oranges cost $2.10.
$2.10 = 210¢
210¢ ÷ 3 = 70¢
70¢ × 2 =140¢

140¢ = $1.40
2 pears and 2 oranges cost $1.40.

9 Fractions

Practice Questions (pp. 124-126)

1. $\frac{3}{4}$
2. $\frac{2}{3}$
3. 36 quarters
4. $\frac{1}{4}$
5. 6
6. Shade any 6 squares.
7. $\frac{1}{2}, \frac{3}{4}, \frac{5}{6}$
8. 6
9. $\frac{5}{6}, \frac{3}{4}, \frac{1}{3}$
10. 1 h

Challenging Problems (pp. 130-134)

1. (a) ◁▷ is the same as ◇
   (b) Two sixths is the same as one third.
   (c) $\frac{2}{6} = \frac{1}{3}$
   or
   (a) △▽△ is the same as ▱
   (b) Three sixths is the same as one half.
   (c) $\frac{3}{6} = \frac{1}{2}$

2. (a) $\frac{1}{\boxed{8}} + \frac{1}{\boxed{8}} = \frac{1}{4}$
   (b) $\frac{1}{\boxed{6}} + \frac{1}{\boxed{6}} + \frac{1}{\boxed{6}} = \frac{1}{2}$

3. 6

4. $\frac{1}{\boxed{8}} + \frac{1}{\boxed{8}} + \frac{1}{\boxed{8}} + \frac{1}{\boxed{8}} = \frac{1}{2}$

5. (a) Answers vary. Some possible
   pairs are: $\frac{1}{10}$ and $\frac{6}{10}$
   $\frac{3}{10}$ and $\frac{4}{10}$

   (b) Answers vary. Some possible
   pairs are: $\frac{7}{10}$ and $\frac{4}{10}$
   $\frac{5}{10}$ and $\frac{2}{10}$

6. Fraction of rod not painted = $\frac{3}{5}$

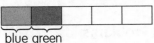

   blue green

7. $\frac{1}{5}$ m or 20 cm

8. $\frac{3}{10}$

9. (a) $\frac{2}{9}$ (b) $\frac{6}{9}$ or $\frac{2}{3}$

10. (a) $\frac{6}{10}$ or $\frac{3}{5}$ (b) $\frac{3}{10}$

10 Time

Practice Questions (pp. 138-141)

1. 1 h 45 min
2. 40 min
3. 9 h 30 min
4. 6:55 p.m.
5. Sunday
6.
   9:40 p.m. $\xrightarrow{4\text{ h}}$ 1:40 a.m.
   $\downarrow$ 20 min
   2:15 a.m. $\xleftarrow{}$ 2:00 a.m.
   $\overset{}{\underset{15\text{ min}}{}}$

   4 h = 4 × 60
       = 240 min
   Number of minutes
   = 240 min + 20 min + 15 min
   = 275 min
7. 6:40 p.m.
8. 234 min
9. 1 h 32 min
10. 2 h 20 min
11. 18 min
12. 31 days

Challenging Problems (pp. 145-149)

1. 7:24 p.m.
2. (a) 6 h 25 min   (b) 9:40 a.m.
3. Friday
4. 120 min
5. 6:00 a.m.
6. (a) 4, 13, 22, 31
   (b) Least number of times = 3;
       Most number of times = 4
7. 12 buses
8. 8:40 p.m.
9. 11 years
10. 1674 min
11. 9 min 2 s
12. (a) Singapore time
       = Geneva time + 7 h
    (b) Sydney time
       = Singapore time + 3 h
    (c) 6:10 a.m. $\xrightarrow{-7\text{ h}}$ 11:10 p.m.
        It is 11:10 p.m. in Geneva.
    (d) 10:25 a.m. $\xrightarrow{-3\text{ h}}$ 7:25 a.m.
        It is 7:25 a.m. in Singapore.

11 Angles

Practice Questions (pp. 153-155)

1. 3 right angles
2. (a) 2   (b) 2
3.

	Angle
Right angle	b, d, g
Smaller than a right angle	a, f
Greater than a right angle	c, e

4. (a) 0 angles   (b) 1 angle
   (c) 4 angles
5.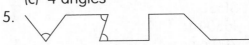

6. (a) 3 angles   (b) 5 angles
7. (a) 3 angles   (b) 3 angles
8. 4

9. D
10. 3 angles

Challenging Problems (pp. 157-160)

1. (a) A, D, G
   (b) A, C, E, F, G, H
   (c) B
   (d) F
2. They are the same.
3. 7 angles
4. 5

5. (a) 16 right angles
   (b) 7 right angles
6. 12 right angles

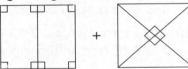

7. 6 angles
8. 2 right angles
9. Answers vary. One example is:
   (a)
   (b)

10. $\frac{1}{4}$ of a turn

12 Perimeter and Area

Practice Questions (pp. 164-166)

1. 48 cm
2. $1530
3. 1530 m
4. 200 cm
5. 36 cm
6. 42 cm
7. 18 cm

8. Area of figure A = 8 square units
   Area of figure B = 5 square units
   Area of figure C = 9 square units

   Perimeter of figure A = 12 units
   Perimeter of figure B = 12 units
   Perimeter of figure C = 12 units

   These figures have the same perimeter.

Challenging Problems (pp. 170-174)

1. (a) 28 cm
   (b) Shift the lines as shown by the arrows.
       They form a rectangle of length 6 cm and width 5 cm.

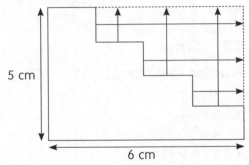

   Perimeter of the figure
   = 5 cm + 6 cm + 5 cm + 6 cm
   = 22 cm
2. (a) 28 cm
   (b) 24 cm
3. 48 cm
4.

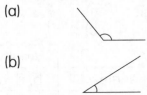

   Number of orange trees = 12
   Number of oranges = 12 × 100
                     = 1200

5. 72 cm

6. Let the length of one rectangle be 3 units.
   Length of the square = 3 units
   Width of the rectangle = 1 unit
   Perimeter of the rectangle
   = 3 units + 1 unit + 3 units + 1 unit
   = 8 units
   8 units ⟶ 16 cm
   1 unit ⟶ 2 cm
   3 units ⟶ 6 cm
   Length of the square = 6 cm
   Perimeter of the square
   = 6 cm × 4
   = 24 cm
7. (a) 6 square units
   (b) 8 square units

13　Mixed Problems 1

Practice Questions (pp. 177-181)

1. 10 cups
2. 11 h 30 min
3. (a) 999　　　　　(b) 1000
4. $3
5. 19, 17, 22
6. 127 or 361
7. 8 cm
8. ☐ = 20
   △ = 90
9. 12 square units
10.

food　　$10
   1 unit ⟶ $10
   3 units ⟶ 3 × $10 = $30
   Amount of pocket money = $30
11. 6 cm
12. 50¢

Challenging Problems (pp. 184-187)

1. 4 llamas

2. 21 times (1, 10, 11, 12, 13, 14, 15, 16, 17, 18, 19, 21, 31, 41, 51, 61, 71, 81, 91, 100)
3. $28.35
4. 78 people
5.

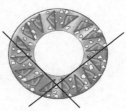

6. 10 years old
7. (a) 90 oz
   (b) (i) Theresa　　(ii) 4 packets
8. 20 beads
9. $5
10. 9 cars
11. Answers vary. Some examples are:

14　Mixed Problems 2

Practice Questions (pp. 190-194)

1. (a) 21, 34　　　　(b) 25, 36
2. (a) $\frac{1}{2}$　　　　(b) $\frac{3}{8}$
   (c) $\frac{1}{4}$
3. 3.55 p.m.
4. Number of students = 13 + 1 + 13
   　　　　　　　　　　= 27
5. 385 g
6. The tennis ball is the biggest while the marble is the smallest. The bigger the ball is, the more space it will occupy.
   (a) The box with tennis balls.
   (b) The box with marbles.
7. Number of handshakes
   = 4 + 3 + 2 + 1
   = 10

8. (a) 120 bags   (b) $360
9. 9 square units
10. Dennis, Esther, Aaron, Cathy, Betty
11. 14 marbles; 50 marbles
12.

2 l	9 l
0	9
2	7
0	7
2	5
0	5
2	3

13. 582 stickers

Challenging Problems (pp. 196-200)

1. 526 parents
2. Number of dots = 21 − 16 = 5
3. A = 0, B = 5, C = 1
4. 6 numbers (141, 252, 363, 474, 585, 696)
5. 175 m
6. 561 (= 765 − 204)
7. $60
8. 304 ÷ 9 = 33 R 7

Number of months	Savings
33	$297
34	$306

Number of months he needs to save = 34
9. 96 (Look for a 2-digit number that is divisible by 6)
10. 4 ways (1 × 36, 2 × 18, 3 × 12, 4 × 9)
11. 54 cm
12. (a)

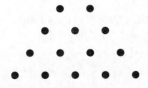

(b) Number of dots
= 1 + 2 + 3 + ... + 9 + 10
= 55

15   Mixed Problems 3

Practice Questions (pp. 203-206)

1. 7 people
2. 5 days
3. $1230
4. 10:42 p.m.
5. Both have the same number of buttons.
6. 648
7. 5 darts (10, 5, 2, 2, 2)
8. $\dfrac{1}{8} + \dfrac{1}{8} + \dfrac{1}{8} + \dfrac{1}{8} = \dfrac{1}{2}$
9. $1525
10. 10; 30
Multiply first number by 3 and add 9 to the product or add 3 to the first number and multiply the sum by 3.

Challenging Problems (pp. 210-215)

1. $220
2. 36 pears
3.

3   4   8
1   5   9
2   6   7

4. 16 snakes and 6 spiders

5. Answers vary. Some examples are:

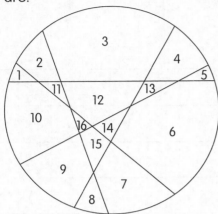

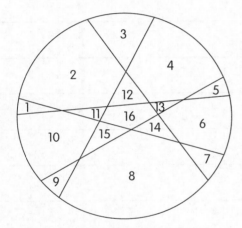

Most number of pieces = 16

6. $\dfrac{1}{8} = \dfrac{1}{4} - \dfrac{1}{\boxed{8}}$

$\dfrac{1}{6} + \dfrac{1}{6} = \dfrac{1}{2} - \dfrac{1}{\boxed{6}}$

7. 4 books
8. (a) 5 erasers   (b) $3
9. 20 cm
10. 7 boys and 6 girls
11. 60 cm
12. 16 right angles

Notes